W9-AKU-783

What's Inside?

Dear Parents,

Are you aware that students can lose up to 25% of their reading and math skills during the summer vacation break away from academics*? While the freedom away from school during the summer break can be a wonderful time in your child's life, the reality is children will experience summer learning loss if they don't practice the skills they developed during the school year. That is why we created Summer Vacation®, a valuable investment in your child's future. Summer Vacation is a fun, entertaining educational program to help your child review skills learned during the previous school year and prepare them for the challenges of the next.

This 6th grade activity workbook has been thoroughly reviewed and recommended by an esteemed panel of teachers. It is packed with fun, skills-based activities for every day of the summer. Some of the activities in this book include:

• New chapter story with fun reading comprehension activities
• New progressive project - "Make model airplanes and explore the theory of flight"
• New removable "history of flight facts" charts
• Solve word problems using addition, subtraction, multiplication and division
• Converting fractions, decimals and percentages
• Place value up to the 100,000,000,000s column
• Place value through 10,000s column in decimals
• Basic geometry
• Constructing and reading bar, line and pie graphs
• Comprehensive grammar and punctuation exercises
• Constructing and reading graphs
• Logic problems
• Brain teasers

It may be beneficial for your child to pick a certain time each day to work on the activities. This consistency will help make participation a habit, and will provide some quality time that will ultimately assist with their educational development.

We hope you and your child enjoy Summer Vacation®!

*Source: Harris Cooper, professor and chairman of the psychology department at the University of Missouri at Columbia.

Summer Vacation®
Teacher Review Panel

Our panel of distinguished educators was instrumental in ensuring that the Summer Vacation® program offers your child maximum educational benefit. This panel provided key ideas and feedback on all aspects of our workbook series. We welcome your feedback.

Please contact us at:
Attn: Summer Vacation, Entertainment Publications, 2125 Butterfield Road, Troy, Michigan 48084
or e-mail us at
summervacation@entertainment.com.

Cathy Cerveny, Baltimore, MD
Maryland Teacher of the Year, 1996
Fifth-grade teacher; Integrated
Language Arts curriculum writer
Served on Maryland's Professional
Standards and Teacher Education Board

Norma Jackson, Keller, TX
Texas Teacher of the Year, 1999
On special assignment as District Writing
Specialist for grades K–5
Second-grade teacher
Summer Activity Writing Specialist

Becky Miller, Mason, OH
Gifted Coordinator for Mason City Schools
Taught elementary grades 3 and 4
Adjunct Professor at
Xavier University

Laurie Sybert, Lake Ozark, MO
Missouri Teacher of the Year, 1999
Second-grade teacher
Elementary Science coordinator
Fulbright Teacher Scholar

Jenlane Gee Matt, Modesto, CA
California Teacher of the Year, 1988
National Teacher of the Year finalist, 1989
Third-grade teacher

Gemma Hoskins, Bel Air, MD
Maryland Teacher of the Year, 1992
Technology Coordinator for school
Former fifth-grade teacher and
elementary teacher specialist

Charles Mercer, Washington, DC
District of Columbia Teacher of the Year, 1999
Worked at NASA's Education Program Office
Elementary Science resource
teacher, PK–6

Denise Johnson, New York, NY
Teacher Center Specialist in Manhattan
Previously taught grades 4–8
Instructor at Brooklyn College

**Richard Scott Griffin,
Mount Holly, NC**
North Carolina Teacher of the Year, 1996
Teaches grades 4-6—all subject areas
Served as Teacher Advisor to State Board
of Education

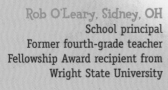

Rob O'Leary, Sidney, OH
School principal
Former fourth-grade teacher
Fellowship Award recipient from
Wright State University

Bruce Fisher, Arcata, CA
California Teacher of the Year, 1991
Teacher for 23 years at
Fortuna Elementary
Distinguished Teacher in Residence
at Humboldt State University

Getting Ready for Sixth Grade

The fifth grade was a time for your child to embrace his or her growing independence, responsibility, and individuality. Seeking ways of satisfying the need to understand the hows and whys of the world, your fifth grader probably started turning more toward friends and peer groups than to parents or caregivers. Your fifth-grade graduate may be able to

- use synonyms, antonyms, homophones, and analogies to build vocabulary.
- recognize and apply all parts of speech.
- appreciate different forms of literature.
- incorporate suspense, dialogue, and figurative language into writing.
- edit writing from knowledge of spelling, punctuation, and grammar and usage.
- form analogies, similes, and metaphors to establish relationships.
- use deductive reasoning to make predictions and inferences in literature.
- expand personal writing in the form of letters, essays, and journal entries.
- condense learning material through note taking, outlines, and summaries.
- use and discuss symbolism and personification (attributing human characteristics to animals or objects) in writing and literature.
- identify, measure, and convert units of length, capacity, and mass in customary and metric units.
- perform operations accurately using whole numbers, fractions, and decimals.
- determine the perimeter of polygons and the area of squares and rectangles.

Grade 6 Skills

The sixth grade will be an exciting and potentially frustrating year as your child enters adolescence. His or her growing autonomy will be illustrated by a growing self-assertion and curiosity. Sixth-grade teachers work to increase students' proficiency in basic skills. Organization will be critical as your child begins to have a different teacher for each subject. By the end of the sixth grade, your child may be able to

- use similes, metaphors, and personification to enhance writing.
- identify and incorporate first-person and third-person point of view in literature and writing.
- use base words, word endings and beginnings, and context clues to decode.
- demonstrate the use of the writing process.
- use research skills to write detailed reports.
- interpret graphs.
- plot coordinates and ordered pairs on a graph.
- find the radius, diameter, and circumference of circles.
- apply abstract reasoning to solve simple algebraic equations.
- work with ratios, proportions, and percents.

How You Can Help

You can help prepare your child for sixth grade by making this Summer Vacation™ book a regular part of your daily routine. Assist your child in the construction of the airplane models and with the additional research and writing activities. Share in the reading of the stories found in this book as a vehicle for discussion and to model reading as an enjoyable experience in your life. The Summer Vacation™ book is designed to help your child retain the skills that he or she developed in fifth grade and to prepare him or her for the challenges of sixth grade.

Hudson's Children

CHAPTER ONE

Cold air poured from the air-conditioning, and Trekk was happy to lie there and let the cool wave wash over him. The day, like the summer, stretched out in front of him with no schedules, no demands, and no need even to see what day it was. "This is great," Trekk thought.

Most summers, it was go, go, go. For as long as Trekk could remember, he and his cousin Terra had spent summers together, finding one adventure after the next. Terra's mother was an archaeologist from New Mexico, and they had been to several of her digs in the Southwest. Other summers they'd been with Trekk's dad, a writer, as he took working vacations to do research on articles he wrote for a New York newspaper.

This year, though, everybody was staying home. Terra's mom was finishing a report on her work, and Trekk's dad had nothing special to do. Trekk felt bad about not missing Terra more, but he was also looking forward to just hanging with his friends. He'd been practicing three-sixties on his skateboard, and he knew that when he landed in sixth grade this fall, he would be landing the jump as well.

"Trekk, wake up. I have news." Trekk roused himself. Was it lunchtime? "I have news," Dad repeated. "We'll see Terra after all."

"Huh? We will?" Trekk responded groggily. "Uh…why?"

"Her mom got a chance to go to Peru. She's going to excavate ruins in the mountains. So Terra's going to be with us."

"Oh. Cool. Okay," Trekk said, but he wondered how the energetic Terra would fit in with his friends and his plans for goofing off. "When does she get here?"

"She doesn't," Dad said. "That's part two of the news. We'll pick her up. I've been assigned to research and report on Henry Hudson."

"Who's Henry Hudson?" Trek asked. "And what are you supposed to write about him?"

"Hudson, like the river," Dad said. "And I haven't any idea what to write about yet. I'm sure I'll know what direction to take once our research is underway."

Trekk groaned. "Who wants to study a dirty old river?" he asked.

"Not the river," Dad grinned, "the Bay. We'll meet Terra in Michigan, and then head north."

"North? What's north of Michigan? Canada?" Trekk was having trouble taking it all in at once.

"Exactly," Dad said. "Western Ontario to be precise. What information do you know" he dragged out poetically, "about the province of Ontario?"

"I'm not sure I know enough about Ontario to be much help," Trekk chimed back. "Can I bring my skateboard?" Dad smiled, more or less.

"Better start packing," he said.

Trekk decided to make the best of it. "Maybe we can come up with an idea for you," he said.

"I'd love it," Dad said. "But even if you don't, I promise you adventure."

Monday

Activity 1

Skill: Simple Sentences

Fill in the empty blocks to make simple sentences. The sentences run across, down and diagonally.

Trekk's		Cousin		_____.
	home	Terra	an	
Trekk's	dad	is	a	_____.
	mother	from	in	
Terra's		_____.		_____.

Math Maze

Find 49,016

- Starting with the number "5" on the left-hand side, you may proceed up, down or horizontally (sideways). The object is to end up with a total of 49,016.

- Each time you cross a "diamond" you must multiply your number by "6." Then add the number in the next circle to your total.

- The last circled number you add to your total should be the "8" in the middle.

- Remember, the numbers in the circle are meant to be added to your total, the "diamonds" mean you multiply by "6."

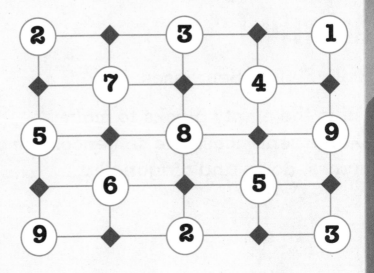

For example:

$5 \blacklozenge 4 = 34$ ($5 \times 6 = 30 + 4 = 34$)

Word Games

Can you figure out which word doesn't belong?
Circle the correct answer.

1. cotton   nylon   silk   wool

2. canine   incisor   dendrite   molar

3. bear   robin   bat   snake

WHAT ARE YOU AFRAID OF?

Match the phobias to their correct definitions.
If you need help, use an encyclopedia or the Internet.

1. hydrophobia

2. bibliophobia

3. pogonophobia

4. taphophobia

5. sciophobia

6. heliophobia

7. graphophobia

8. arachnophobia

a. fear of beards

b. fear of spiders

c. fear of the sun

d. fear of shadows

e. fear of books

f. fear of water

g. fear of graves

h. fear of writing

ULTIMATE SCRAMBLE

Directions: Unscramble the letters below to form words.
Unscramble the circled letters from each word to solve the riddle.

1 andrclae ⬭☐☐⬭☐☐⬭☐

2 nulch ☐☐☐☐⬭

3 pleap ☐⬭☐☐⬭

4 neatatdenc ☐⬭⬭☐☐☐☐☐☐⬭

5 scerse ⬭☐☐☐☐⬭

Hint: Mrs. Johnson owned a cat, but her
favorite student was the...

Answer:

⬭⬭⬭⬭⬭⬭⬭'⬭

⬭⬭⬭

Mega Math

Use pennies, nickels, dimes, quarters, half dollars, and silver dollars to solve these problems.

Tom has saved enough money to buy his favorite CD. The CD costs $9.90. He has an equal number of four different coins. Which four coins does he have? How many of each coin does he have?

Place Values

Hundred Billions 100,000,000,000s	Ten Billions 10,000,000,000s	Billions 1,000,000,000s	Hundred Millions 100,000,000s	Ten Millions 10,000,000s	Millions 1,000,000s
Hundred Thousands 100,000s	Ten Thousands 10,000s	Thousands 1,000s	Hundreds 100s	Tens 10s	Ones 1s

Write out each number in expanded notation.

Example: 99,286,611,357

90,000,000,000 + 9,000,000,000 + 200,000,000 + 80,000,000 + 6,000,000 + 600,000 + 10,000 + 1,000 + 300 + 50 + 7

1. 65,444,299

_____

2. 1,967,822

_____

3. 479,586,286,533

_____

4. 831,481,915

_____

Thursday

Balance the Checking Account

Calculate the weekly balance for the checking account. Deposits are adding money to the account, so you must add. Withdrawals are taking money out of the account, so you must subtract.

Date	Deposit	Withdrawal	Balance
Jan. 2nd	$208.00		$675.00
Jan. 9th		$88.11	
Jan. 16th		$256.62	
Jan. 23rd	$1,211.47		
Jan. 30th		$118.98	
Feb. 6th	$526.50		
Feb. 13th		$733.69	
Feb. 20th	$64.99		
Feb. 27th		$412.53	
March 6th	$75.75		
March 13th		$67.88	
March 20th	$298.98		

PROGRESSIVE WORDS

Can you get from the first word to the last by changing just one letter in each step?

Each word must be a real word!

Example: Change DIVER to MAJOR

DIVER
DINER
MINER
MANOR
MAJOR

RIDER

_____

_____

_____

_____

HOPES

FAMOUS PEOPLE FACTS

Match the Facts to the Famous Person!

If you need help, use an encyclopedia or the Internet.

1. Thomas Edison

2. Jim Thorpe

3. William Howard Taft

4. Christopher Columbus

A. A Native American, he excelled in all sports. In 1950, he was voted the Athlete of the Century. He won two Olympic gold medals and played pro baseball and football.

B. He sailed west looking for a quick trade route to India. Instead, he discovered the New World in 1492. Believing he was in India he erroneously called the natives Indians.

C. He has over 1,000 patents to his credit. He is best known for perfecting the incandescent light bulb but is rumored to have been afraid of the dark! His nickname was the "Wizard of Menlo Park"— the location of his laboratory in New Jersey.

D. The 27th U.S. president, he weighed over 300 pounds. According to reports he once got stuck in the White House bathtub!

Friday

If you could live for 500 years, would you? Why or why not? What type of things can you imagine seeing? What events can you imagine experiencing? What would the future hold?

_____

_____

_____

_____

_____

_____

_____

_____

_____

_____

_____

_____

_____

_____

_____

_____

WORD PUZZLE

Mystery Word

	A	B	C	D	E
1	H	O	X	V	N
2	T	L	W	U	D
3	A	N	S	T	G
4	F	I	K	C	B
5	E	M	P	O	R

- Use the box above to fill in the letters below.

- Each letter of the mystery word will use only one of the letters from each column below (top or bottom letter).

- Can you decipher the mystery instrument?

C3	B2	A3	B1	B4	E1	B3	D3
D4	A3	C1	E5	C5	A1	A5	C4

13

Exploring Flight:
The Science of Flight

Adult supervision is recommended.

Introduction to the Project

Humans have long dreamed of soaring high in the air like birds, but for centuries, many believed that if we were meant to fly, we would have wings. That was before the science of aviation took flight. As your child uses hands-on activities to study the basic concepts of aerodynamics, the magic of flight comes alive. Working with objects such as balloons and paper models, your child will learn the physical forces that act upon objects in flight as well as how those forces can manipulate and control flight patterns.

These enrichment activities require your child to use skills such as logic and analysis to follow directions, make inferences and observations, and draw conclusions. This experience teaches your child how the scientific method is used to test a hypothesis and how the introduction of variables can affect test results.◆

Master Materials List

8 sheets of 8.5 in. x 11 in. (21.6 cm x 27.9 cm) paper

scissors

2 sheets of colored construction paper

paper clips (at least 30)

masking tape

4 clothespins

4 paper muffin liners

tape measure or yardstick

ruler

pen (blue or black)

box of crayons or nontoxic, washable colored markers

tape (masking tape or invisible tape)

fishing line

2 plastic straws or small sticks

wax paper or plastic wrap

nontoxic glue or paste suitable for paper

pencil

helium balloon

bucket

large plastic self-sealing bag

foam cup

penny

safety pin

(Optional)

nontoxic, washable paints

onion, parchment, or wax paper, cut to 8.5 in. × 11 in. (21.6 cm × 27.9 cm) size

Manila file folder

cereal box

What do you think air is made of? Although air is invisible, it actually has substance, or mass, and weight. Air presses down on the earth all the time. We usually do not notice air pressure unless we are underwater, where the pressure is greater, or when we fly in the sky, where the pressure is less. Air pushes an airplane forward and helps keep it up in the sky.

Four main forces act on an airplane to make it fly: weight, lift, thrust and drag. In general, weight pulls a plane down, lift pulls a plane up, thrust pushes a plane forward, and drag pulls a plane backward. *See Figure 1.*

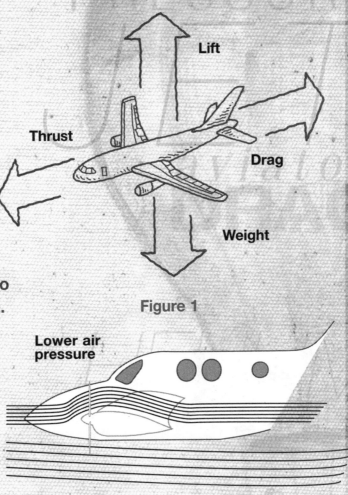

Figure 1

Figure 2

Materials

8.5 in. x 11 in. (21.6 cm x 27.9 cm) paper
scissors

Directions

In the early 1700s, mathematician Daniel Bernoulli discovered that the faster air moves, the lower its pressure is. Because of an airplane wing's teardrop shape, air moves faster over the wing than under it. This causes the air pressure pushing down on the top of the wing to be lower than the pressure pushing up. See *Figure 2.* The difference in pressure causes suction, which pulls the wings up—a process called lift.

1. To see Bernoulli's principle at work, take an 8.5 in. x 11 in. (21.6 cm x 27.9 cm) sheet of paper.

2. Cut the paper in half lengthwise.

3. Hold the short end of one strip of paper to your lips using the forefinger and thumb of both hands as shown. Blow over the top edge of the paper. Watch what happens. See *Figure 3.*

Figure 3

More Mega Math

Each of the symbols represents a number between 1 - 10. Can you figure out which number should fill in the blank?

■● = ▲▲

●■▲ = ■●●●

●●●● = _____

Fractions, Decimals & Percentages

Example: $\frac{15}{100}$ = .15 = 15%

Fill in the blanks below.

1 $\frac{1}{100}$ = .____ = ____%

2 ⎯ = .13 = ____%

3 ⎯ = .____ = 66%

4 $\frac{77}{100}$ = .____ = ____%

5 ⎯ = .____ = 98%

6 $\frac{33}{100}$ = .____ = ____%

7 ⎯ = .32 = ____%

8 $\frac{42}{100}$ = .____ = ____%

Similes, Metaphors and Personification

Simile: compares two things using the word like or as.

Metaphor: compares two things without using the word like or as.

Personification: compares two things by giving human qualities to things that are not human.

A. simile   B. metaphor   C. personification

Label each sentence as A, B or C.

1 He ran as fast as a cougar. _____

_____

2 The waves crashed like thunder. _____

_____

3 The lion's mane was a wreath of fur. _____

_____

4 The rain danced across the schoolyard. _____

_____

5 The sleeping snake could have been mistaken for a coil of rope. _____

_____

6 Her face was as white as a ghost. _____

_____

7 Twilight tiptoed into the daylight. _____

_____

8 The dandelions on the lawn appeared to be green and yellow carpeting. _____

_____

Hudson's Children

CHAPTER TWO

Terra headed to the baggage claim area of the Detroit Metro Airport to meet Trekk and his dad. She saw Trekk before he saw her. She looked at Trekk the same way she did every summer when they first saw each other—trying to see what was different. Terra noticed that he was taller than she expected, and what on earth was he doing to his hair? She could see that he was looking at her in the same deliberate way as he and his dad got closer to where she stood waiting.

"Hey," she said to Trekk. "Hi, Uncle Phil."

"Hi, Terra," Trekk's dad said. "How was your flight?"

"Good, really. I'm pretty used to it now." At first, when Terra had flown alone it had seemed scary, like rowing across a lake when you couldn't see the other side. The flight attendants were always nice to her, and she was comfortable now. Trekk had felt the same way when it was his turn to go West, and it was one of the things they always talked about.

Uncle Phil looked different to Terra, too, and she said so to Trekk later as they loaded their camping equipment. Trekk's dad had borrowed a truck and gear from an old college friend in Michigan, which is why Terra had met her uncle and cousin there. "It's not been a great year in the city," Trekk said, "and I think Dad's just tired. I don't think he had to come out here. I think he just wanted to. Where do you suppose these could fit?" he said, as he waggled a pair of canoe paddles.

They set off the next morning, and Terra marveled at the green countryside in this part of the country. They went northwest at first, to the west edge of the state along Lake Michigan, up past the apple and cherry orchards. They camped the first night in a town called White Cloud. As soon as their tents were raised and a fire built, Terra and Trekk went for a moonlight hike. The night air smelled of campfires and pine, and Terra felt as though she were moving back in time as well as away from town.

"I love it, the smell of it, as if you were breathing in the whole world at its best," Terra announced with a relaxed sigh.

"I do, too," Trekk said. "But just wait until tomorrow. We're going sailing."

Monday

Activity 2

Skill: Reading Comprehension

1. How did Trekk look different to Terra as she left the airplane?

   _____

   _____

2. How have Terra's feelings about flying alone changed?

   _____

   _____

3. Why did the three meet in Michigan?

   _____

   _____

4. Which direction did they go when they began to travel?

   _____

5. What crops did they observe?

   _____

6. What do Terra, Trekk and Trekk's dad do in White Cloud, Michigan?

   _____

7. What does the group plan to do the next day?

   _____

Odd Number Out

Tuesday

Can you figure out which number doesn't belong?
Circle the correct answer.

1. 24   72   108   63   12

2. 33   132   71   66   11

3. 56   14   28   92   98

Adverbial Phrases

An adverbial phrase is a group of words that acts as an adverb.
They tell where, when, how or to what extent.

Example: The boat sped (along the river.)

Circle the adverbial phrases in the sentences below.

1. She ate her hamburger in a hurry.

2. He lost his watch in the back yard.

3. You better run as fast as you can.

4. My uncle works nights and sleeps during the day.

5. My brother ran on the treadmill for an hour.

6. The mechanic tuned the car with precision.

HEY OLD SPORT!

Match the terms with their sport.
If you need help, use an encyclopedia or the Internet.

1. balk

a. basketball

2. fair catch

b. golf

3. two-line pass

c. football

4. takedown

d. tennis

5. dismount

e. baseball

6. fault

f. hockey

7. over and back

g. gymnastics

8. hazard

h. wrestling

Wednesday

PHOTO MATCH

Match the photo to the name of the sport.

 a

 b

 c

 d

 e

 f

 g

 h

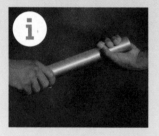 i

 j

 k

 l

 m

 n

_____ 1. gymnastics

_____ 2. hockey

_____ 3. lacrosse

_____ 4. cricket

_____ 5. fishing

_____ 6. archery

_____ 7. basketball

_____ 8. baseball

_____ 9. football

_____ 10. golf

_____ 11. horseracing

_____ 12. lawnbowling

_____ 13. soccer

_____ 14. track & field

Mega Math

Can you solve the following problem? Assign different values for consonants and vowels. Can you detect a rule for solving the unknown amount?

Jamal went to the store and bought groceries for dinner. He bought the following items:

- Hamburger $3.60
- Buns $1.30
- Potato Chips   ?

How much did the potato chips cost?
What's the rule?

Punctuation & Capitalization Quiz

Punctuate and capitalize the paragraph below:

sara couldn't wait for summer vacation to begin her

family was planning a trip to europe mom when are we

leaving for our trip asked sara we will leave on june 30

answered sara's mother

Finding Radius, Diameter and Circumference

Circumference measures the distance around a circle. To find circumference of a circle, multiply the diameter by three. To find diameter, multiply the radius by two. To find the radius, divide diameter by two. Fill in the missing data below. The first one is done for you.

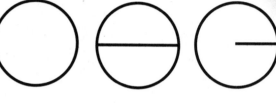

1. Circumference   2. Diameter   3. Radius

Circumference	Diameter	Radius
1. 6 feet	2 feet	1 foot
2.	14 cm	
3. 36 meters		
4.		4 mm
5.		812 cm
6.	25 miles	
7. 933 inches		
8.		51.2 yards
9.	.88 km	
10. 1,263 feet		
11.	7,612 cm	
12.		.115 mm
13. 573 meters		
14.	.999 cm	

PROGRESSIVE WORDS

Can you get from the first word to the last by changing just one letter in each step?

Each word must be a real word!

TWINE

_____

_____

_____

_____

SPOTS

FAMOUS PEOPLE FACTS

Match the Facts to the Famous Person!

If you need help, use an encyclopedia or the Internet.

1. James Naismith

2. Amelia Earhart

3. Mel Blanc

4. Susan B. Anthony

A. The voice behind Bugs Bunny and many other cartoon characters. He was often referred to as the "Man of 1,000 Voices."

B. Inventor of the great American game of basketball. In fact, he wasn't American at all. He was Canadian! Born in Ontario, Canada, he worked as a physical education teacher in Springfield, Massachusetts. He invented basketball as an indoor game to be played during New England's harsh winters.

C. A crusader for women's rights. She fought to gain suffrage, the right to vote, for women in America. She was once arrested for casting a ballot in the election of 1872! Her likeness was portrayed on silver dollars in the late 1970s.

D. She was the first woman to fly across the Atlantic Ocean. She did that in 1928. In 1932 she crossed again, this time solo, and set a record for speed. In 1937 she attempted to circle the globe at the equator. Her plane lost radio contact and was never heard from again.

Friday

You are a superhero and it is your job to fight crime. However, it is up to you to create which superpowers you will have and what you are capable of doing. Using this page, describe your superpowers (how they work, what they do) and what kind of situations you will use them in. You can even write your own adventure!

_____

_____

_____

_____

_____

_____

_____

_____

_____

_____

_____

_____

_____

_____

_____

_____

WORD PUZZLE

Word Box

D	R	A	F	T
R				R
A				E
F				S
T	R	E	S	S

Fill in the word square above using these nine letters:
- three of the letter "E"
- two each of the letters "F" and "R"
- one each of the letters "I" and "N"

This is a total of 25 letters (including the letters already given). The resulting words can be read both across and down.

Flying Is a Weighty Matter

Adult supervision is recommended.

When your pencil falls off your desk and onto the ground, you are witnessing the force of gravity. Weight is a measure of how gravity, or the pull toward earth, affects an object. In aeronautics, lift and weight are closely related: The heavier the object, the greater the amount of lift needed to make the object fly. If a plane had no lift, its weight would pull it to the ground. ◆

Falling to Earth

Materials

2 sheets of 8.5 in. × 11 in.
   (21.6 cm × 27.9 cm) paper

Directions

See how the forces of weight and lift influence each other and affect flight time.

1. Take two identical sheets of paper, and crumple one into a ball.

2. Holding your arms up in the air, drop the flat and crumpled paper from an equal height at the same time.

3. Which paper hits the ground first? What force explains this result?

_____

_____

_____

_____

Holding Up Objects With Water and Air

Materials

bucket
water
large plastic self-sealing bag
foam cup
penny

Directions

Just like water, air is fluid and has substance. Try this experiment to see how water can support weight.

1. Fill the bucket about three-quarters full with water.

2. Place a plastic bag in the bucket, and fill the bag halfway with water. Squeeze out all the air in the bag before closing it tightly.

3. Lift the bag out of the water, and notice how heavy it feels. Place the bag back in the water, while holding the bag. Notice how light the bag now feels. This is because the bucket's water is holding up the bag's water.

4. Next, take a foam cup and place it on the water in the bucket. Why doesn't the cup sink? The cup floats on top of the water because it is lighter than the same amount of water underneath it. Objects float in matter (such as air or water) that can support them.

5. Place a penny on the water in the bucket. What happens to it and why?

_____
_____
_____

Let's Take a Balloon Ride!

Materials

helium balloon
string
paper clips

Directions

Helium is lighter than air. Follow this experiment to see how much weight is needed to stabilize a helium balloon in the air so that it neither rises nor falls.

1. Tie a string to a helium balloon if it doesn't already have one.

2. Tie a loop at the bottom of the string. Attach a paper clip to the loop, and then add more paper clips until the balloon is perfectly balanced in the air. How many paper clips are needed?

_____
_____
_____

If a normal paper clip weighs about .01 oz. (.28 g), how much weight was needed to stabilize the balloon?

_____
_____
_____

Grid Logic

For examples on how to complete Grid Logic, read the instructions at the back of the book.

	Nathan	Tino	Vanessa	Azra	Maple	Oak	Birch	Spruce
Kamali								
Rodriguez								
Bahaligia								
Feinstein								
Maple								
Oak								
Birch								
Spruce								

Mrs. Osaki's fifth grade class is doing a science project on trees. Azra and her three friends each were allowed to choose a tree to study. Based on the clues below, can you determine each child's first and last name and the tree that they studied?

1. Nathan, the Bahaligia boy, and the child who studied the oak tree all lived in the same neighborhood.

2. Vanessa, the child who studied the maple tree, and the Kamali child often ate lunch together.

3. The Rodriguez girl studied a tree that was a conifer, while all the other children studied deciduous trees.

4. By researching his science project, Tino found that he was studying a tree with white, paper-like bark that peels easily, while the Feinstein boy found that his type of tree is capable of producing edible syrup.

Prefixes

Prefixes are added to the beginning of base words. Add a prefix to each word below and then write a sentence using the new word.

Prefixes: mis, dis, re, un, non, pre
Base Words: appear, understand, view, read, sure, stop

1 _____ appear _____

_____

2 _____ understand _____

_____

3 _____ view _____

_____

4 _____ read _____

_____

5 _____ sure _____

_____

6 _____ stop _____

_____

Hudson's Children

CHAPTER THREE

Trekk, his dad, and Terra drove early the next morning to Petoskey, a city on Lake Michigan. There, Trekk's dad had arranged a one-day sailing class in small, single-person sailboats called Optimist Dinghies.

Trekk was impatient, though, as the instructor, Mr. Guindon, explained the parts of a boat and how they worked. His impatience grew when he noticed the boats dancing on the waves in the harbor. Trekk's attention returned when the instructor talked about how to sail the dinghy. Mr. Guindon explained some important sailing terms—sailing with the wind; tacking or moving into the wind; and the fastest way, sailing across the wind. "Always let the wind lead you," he said. "If it shifts, you must be ready."

Mr. Guindon helped them rig their boats, attaching the bottom bar, or boom, to the foot of the sail, and then hoisting the sail. At last, they untied the lines and moved away from the dock. "All right," shouted Trekk as the breeze picked up and his dinghy began to move. Suddenly, his boat was "luffing," or stalling, because the wind had changed direction. With some wild motions of the boom and the rudder, Trekk got moving again.

Fumbling at first, everyone soon began to get better at controlling the boats. Terra loved it, feeling as if she were partners with the breeze. Trekk happily coached himself aloud, and his dad smiled, looking relaxed. Suddenly the wind increased. Terra sensed it instantly, and adjusted her rudder and sail to catch it. The boat skipped ahead. Trekk caught it too, and extended his sail as far as he could. He was sailing across the wind, and the dinghy rapidly picked up speed. "Yahoooooo!" he shouted, rising.

"Trekk, don't stand," Dad called, but Trekk was too far away to hear, and took a skateboarder's pose as the dinghy bounced through the water. At that moment the boat hit a wave hard. Losing his balance, Trekk leaned on the rudder and the boat spun. The sail shot across the boat, swinging the boom like a baseball bat. The boom cracked Trekk hard in the knees, and his dinghy turned over.

Underwater, Trekk was stunned by the cold and the swiftness of what had happened. He bobbed to the surface quickly, grateful for his life jacket.

Mr. Guindon, in a small motorboat, reached him first and fished him out. Although Mr. Guindon said that this could have happened to anyone, Trekk felt foolish. Not everyone, he admitted to himself, pretends to be skateboarding.

That evening, as Trekk sat rubbing his sore knees, Terra sat down and grinned, "I guess that's why they call it a boom, huh?"

"Funny," Trekk said.

Monday

Activity 3

Skill: Clarifying

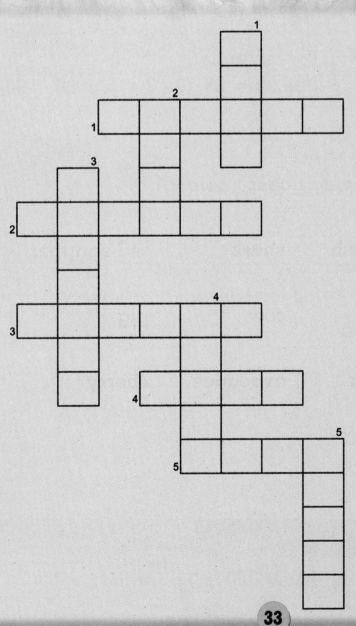

Across

1. Sailing _____ the wind is fastest.

2. Used to steer a sailboat

3. The type of sailboat Terra and Trekk sailed

4. What moves a sailing vessel

5. To move a sailboat into the wind

Down

1. What swept across the deck when the wind changed

2. How the water felt when Trekk fell

3. Stalling a sailboat by going directly into the wind

4. To raise a sail

5. Where Trekk was struck

Math Maze

Race for 350!

- Starting at the top with the number "48" and ending with the number "31," choose the correct path down to the bottom that will result in 350.

- Each time you cross a "triangle" you must subtract three from your number. The circled numbers are to be added—no subtraction or multiplication.

- You must stay on the lines to reach the 350 figure.

- Remember, each triangle is worth -3.

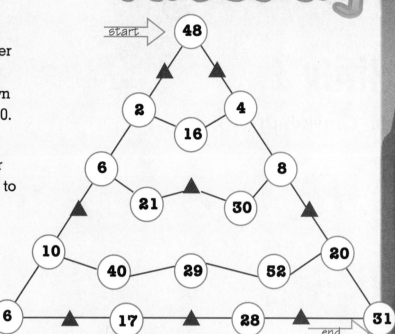

For example:

8 ▲ 20 = 25 (8 - 3 = 5 + 20 = 25)

Word Games

Can you figure out which word doesn't belong?

1. carp · swordfish · shark · red snapper

2. goat · sheep · cow · pig

3. peach · banana · avacados · cherry

IT'S ALL GREEK TO ME

Match the latin names to the animal.
If you need help, use an encyclopedia or the Internet.

1. Felis catus

2. Panthera leo

3. Canis familiaris

4. Equus caballus

5. Orycteropus afer

6. Carassius auratus

7. Orcinus orca

8. Homo sapiens

a. dog

b. horse

c. aardvark

d. cat

e. human

f. lion

g. goldfish

h. killer whale

ULTIMATE SCRAMBLE

Directions: Unscramble the letters below to form words. Unscramble the circled letters from each word to solve the riddle.

1. snabaan

2. tipaerm

3. levvoe

4. uljgne

5. hykucn

Hint: The simian's mother's brother was a...

Answer:

○○○○○○'○

○○○○○

Mega Math

Use pennies, nickels, dimes, quarters, half dollars, and silver dollars to solve these problems.

Jennifer wants to buy a new pair of blue jeans. The jeans she picked out cost $19.00. She has the exact amount. She has an even number of 5 separate coins. Which five coins is she going to pay with? How many of each?

Multiplication of Fractions

When multiplying fractions, multiply across, then reduce the fraction. Match each equation to the correct missing number.

Example: $\dfrac{3}{4} \times \dfrac{2}{9} = \dfrac{6}{36} = \dfrac{1}{6}$

① $\dfrac{2}{3} \times \dfrac{3}{3} = \dfrac{2}{\quad}$

② $\dfrac{8}{5} \times \dfrac{5}{\quad} = 1$

③ $\dfrac{7}{8} \times \dfrac{4}{5} = \dfrac{7}{10}$

④ $\dfrac{3}{\quad} \times \dfrac{7}{9} = \dfrac{7}{18}$

⑤ $\dfrac{6}{7} \times \dfrac{2}{6} = \dfrac{2}{7}$

⑥ $\dfrac{5}{9} \times \dfrac{1}{5} = \dfrac{1}{\quad}$

ⓐ 8

ⓑ 9

ⓒ 2

ⓓ 6

ⓔ 3

ⓕ 7

Pie Graphs

Total Cities A-F Population = 500,500

To find the population for each individual city, change the percent to a decimal and multiply by the total population of 500,500. The first one is done for you.

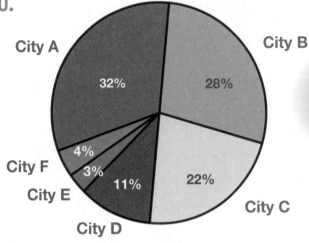

City A 32%
City B 28%
City F 4%
City E 3%
City D 11%
City C 22%

City Name	Percent	Decimal	Population
City A	32%	.32	160,160
City B	28%		
City C	22%		
City D	11%		
City E	3%		
City F	4%		

PROGRESSIVE WORDS

Can you get from the first word to the last by changing just one letter in each step?

Each word must be a real word!

MALLS

_____

_____

_____

_____

PIPER

FAMOUS PEOPLE FACTS

Match the Facts to the Famous Person!

If you need help, use an encyclopedia or the Internet.

1. Rosa Parks

2. Thomas Jefferson

3. Mark Twain

4. Sally Ride

A. Third U.S. president and author of the Declaration of Independence. This revolutionary document proclaimed the natural rights of men—including freedom. Ironically, he was a slave owner.

B. His real name is Samuel Clemens. He was a former riverboat captain along the Mississippi and is considered one of America's greatest authors. His works include "Tom Sawyer" and "Huckleberry Finn."

C. An astrophysicist and NASA astronaut, she became America's first woman in space aboard the space shuttle Challenger in 1983.

D. She has been called the mother of the civil rights movement. While living in segregated Montgomery, Alabama, she refused to give up her bus seat to a white passenger and was arrested. Her trial gained recognition for the civil rights movement.

Friday

Congratulations! You have just been elected President of the United States. So after all the parties, it's time to get down to business. Discuss your plan for improving the country and our various problems.

_____

_____

_____

_____

_____

_____

_____

_____

_____

_____

_____

_____

_____

_____

_____

_____

WORD PUZZLE

Mystery Word

	A	B	C	D	E
1	Q	F	K	E	T
2	C	P	I	E	H
3	S	C	A	T	O
4	O	I	Z	N	R
5	U	C	L	W	B

- Use the box above to fill in the letters below.
- Each letter of the mystery word will use only one of the letters from each column below (top or bottom letter).
- Can you decipher the mystery vegetable?

E5	E4	A4	A2	B3	C2	C5	B4
C4	A5	B3	B3	E2	C1	D4	C1

Exploring Flight:
Spinning Maple Seeds
Adult supervision is recommended.

Thrust is the push planes need to move forward. According to Bernoulli's principle, lift is produced when there is a difference in air pressure above and below the wing.

The same theory can be applied to airplane propellers. Air in front of a propeller blade moves faster than air behind it, lowering the air pressure. Lower air pressure in front of a propeller blade thrusts a plane forward, just like lower air pressure above a wing lifts a plane into the air.

Many aviators rely on spinning propellers to give their aircraft the thrust needed to push them through the air. Maple seeds offer scientists a way to study how nature has designed a "perfect propeller" that spins in the air as it floats to the ground. Bernoulli's principle applies to a simple maple seed as well as to the most sophisticated modern aircraft. ◆

Materials
construction paper

scissors

3 paper clips

Directions
Although maple seeds come in a wide variety of shapes and sizes, all of them spin. It is surprisingly difficult to make a model of a maple seed that spins in the same way.
See whether you can duplicate nature's "perfect propeller."

1. Cut out the three maple seed templates on the right.

2. Use the templates to trace outlines on construction paper, and cut out construction paper seeds. Label the three seeds "A," "B" and "C."

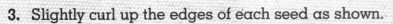

3. Slightly curl up the edges of each seed as shown.

4. Holding the seeds level, drop them one by one from a height of at least 5 feet (1.5 meters).

5. If a seed does not spin, experiment with adjusting the shape of the seed. For example, curl the edges of the seed down, or slightly fold the edge of a seed up or down to add a flap.

6. Experiment with creating your own designs of maple seeds.

When you finish conducting your experimental test flights, answer the following questions. You may need to conduct several tests to confirm your answers.

1. What effect does the shape of the seed seem to have on its ability to spin in the air?

_____

_____

_____

2. How does curling or adding a flap to a seed seem to affect the spin and speed at which it falls to the ground?

_____

_____

_____

3. Which design spins the most like a maple seed? Is it A, B, C or one of your own designs? Why?

_____

_____

_____

More Mega Math

Each of the symbols represents a number between 1 - 10. Can you figure out which number should fill in the blank?

Suffixes

Suffixes are added to the end of base words. Add a suffix to each word below and then write a sentence using the new word.

Suffixes: less, able, ance, ment, ness, ly
Base Words: agree, hope, believe, happy, kind, appear

1 _____

2 _____

3 _____

4 _____

5 _____

6 _____

Calculating Discount Percentages

Match the correct percentages with the sale price. To find out the percentage, divide the amount saved by the total amount.

Example: Regular Price $200 $50 \div 200 = .25 = 25\%$
                  Save $50

1 Regular Price $100   **a** 10%
     Save $15

2 Regular Price $60   **b** 30%
     Save $6

3 Regular Price $48   **c** 50%
     Save $19.20

4 Regular Price $90   **d** 15%
     Save $27

5 Regular Price $250   **e** 40%
     Save $50

6 Regular Price $782   **f** 20%
     Save $391

Hudson's Children

CHAPTER FOUR

Trekk would like to have stayed in Petoskey to improve his sailing skills, but his dad was ready to move north. They quickly covered the forty miles to Mackinaw City, where Lake Huron meets Lake Michigan. "We'll cross into the Upper Peninsula here," Trekk's dad said. Trekk whistled at the size of the bridge they had to cross.

"That's some bridge," he said.

"It's five times the length of the Brooklyn Bridge. From the time it was built in the 1950s until 1998, the Mackinac Bridge was the longest suspension bridge in the world," his dad pointed out.

"Where's the longest?" Terra asked.

"Japan, I think," her uncle said. "And then one in Denmark, and then 'Mighty Mac.'" As they drove over the bridge, Trekk saw that he could look through the deck at the Straits of Mackinac two hundred feet below. The truck tires growled over the open steel grid.

"Why is it open like that?" Trekk asked.

"So the wind goes through," his dad replied. "The bridge moves in high winds, but it doesn't sway."

"You don't think about bridges moving around, do you?" Terra asked.

"I don't want to, either," said Trekk as he peered at the Straits far below.

They went on north through the Upper Peninsula past the Hiawatha National Forest. "Sault Ste. Marie, guys," Trekk's dad said as he approached the town. "Gateway to Canada." Terra noticed that her uncle was veering off course and heading toward the west of town. "You're going to the shipwreck museum, aren't you?" She grinned at the puzzled Trekk. "I looked at the map."

At the Great Lakes Shipwreck Museum, near Whitefish Point and its old lighthouse, they moved from exhibit to exhibit. The danger of the five lakes became apparent as they discovered that more than 6,000 ships and 30,000 lives had been lost. They learned about the giant Edmund Fitzgerald, which disappeared, crew and all, during a November storm. Trekk and Terra looked a long time at the bell of the doomed ship, recovered twenty years after the event, and they listened to a tape of a song about the tragedy. On the drive back to Sault Ste. Marie, Trekk shivered as he thought of his five minutes underwater when his little boat had capsized.

"On to Canada," his Dad said when they arrived back in Sault Ste. Marie. He began to sing the Canadian national anthem, "O, Canada!"

"Where does he get this stuff?" Terra said, rolling her eyes.

"I think he plans it," Trekk said. "I just wish he had practiced it."

Monday

Activity 4

Skill: Verbs

Choose the correct answer for each question.
Circle your choice.

1. Trekk would have liked to remain longer in Petoskey to
   a. examine the bridge more carefully.
   b. improve his sailing skills.
   c. learn more about shipwrecks.
   d. apologize to Mr. Guindon.

2. When Trekk first saw the Mackinac Bridge, he
   a. sang "O Canada."
   b. chimed in with a poem.
   c. whistled in amazement.
   d. peered over the deck.

3. The Straits of Mackinac are where
   a. Lake Erie joins Lake Superior.
   b. Lake Huron becomes Lake Ontario.
   c. Lake Michigan empties into Lake Ontario.
   d. Lake Huron connects to Lake Michigan.

4. The Mackinac Bridge has an open deck to
   a. allow the wind to pass through.
   b. permit large freighters to pass below it.
   c. create openings for viewing the Straits below.
   d. encourage walkers to use the bridge.

5. After they crossed the Mackinac Bridge, the travelers
   a. headed west to Whitefish Point.
   b. studied the map of Canada.
   c. toured the town of St. Ignace.
   d. went north through the Upper Peninsula.

6. The freighter Edmund Fitzgerald
   a. was converted into a museum.
   b. grounded on Whitefish Point.
   c. disappeared during a storm.
   d. survived a furious storm.

Odd Number Out

Can you figure out which number doesn't belong?
Circle the correct answer.

1   36   20   16   9   64

2   25   4   49   42   36

3   1   16   64   81   56

Comparative and Superlative

Most comparative forms of adjectives end in "er." Most
superlative forms of adjectives end in "est." Fill in the
blanks below. The first one is done for you.

Word	Comparative	Superlative
1 large	larger	largest
2 high		
3 big		
4 quick		
5 long		
6 fast		

COUNTRY CURRENCIES

Match the currencies with their countries.
If you need help, use an encyclopedia or the Internet.

1. Brazil

2. China

3. Mexico

4. India

5. Israel

6. Russia

7. South Africa

8. Japan

a. yen

b. rand

c. réal

d. yuan

e. peso

f. shekel

g. rupee

h. rouble

Clueless Crossword *Wednesday*

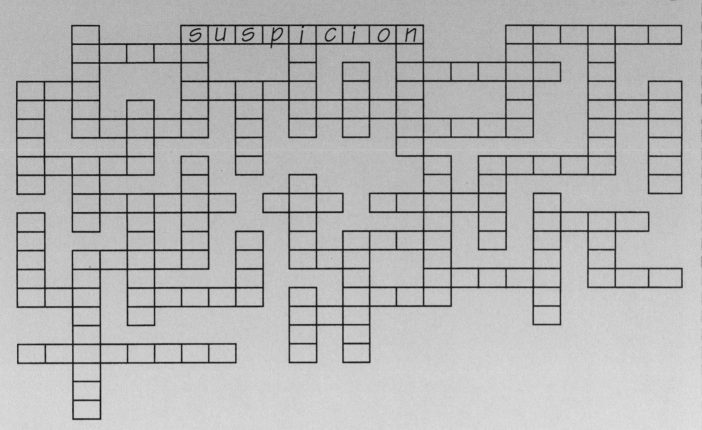

s u s p i c i o n

This crossword is unlike any you've seen because it doesn't have any clues! Instead, fill in the grid according to the length of the word. We've filled in the first word for you.

3-letter words
bee
eel
end
her
rot
she
sky

4-letter words
also
arcs
cars
edge
feet
frog
ibis
item
odds

5-letter words
angle
debar
earth
gamma
lanai
leave
light
llama
lunar
nails
nerve
pupil
thumb
trace
trams

6-letter words
agreed
banded
breath
broken
Indian
nature
nickel
safety
sailor
stilts

7-letter words
ideally
idiotic
nacelle
nankeen

8-letter words
daffodil
daughter
road maps

9-letter words
suspicion
therefore

Mega Math

Can you solve the following problem? Assign different values for consonants and vowels. Can you detect a rule for solving the unknown amount?

Keshia needed birthday party supplies. She bought:

- Balloons $4.75
- Candles $4.00
- Favors   ?

How much did the favors cost? What's the rule?

Ratio Quiz

Match each statement to the correct set of numbers.

1. Two numbers that add to 36 and are in a 1:2 ratio
2. Two numbers that add to 130 and are in a 6:7 ratio
3. Two numbers that add to 50 and are in a 4:1 ratio
4. Two numbers that add to 48 and are in a 1:1 ratio
5. Two numbers that add to 70 and are in a 5:2 ratio
6. Two numbers that add to 170 and are in a 5:12 ratio

a. 40, 10
b. 50, 20
c. 12, 24
d. 50, 120
e. 24, 24
f. 60, 70

Thursday

Finding Area

Find the area for each shape.
Rectangle Area = length x width
Triangle Area = $\frac{1}{2}$ x base x height

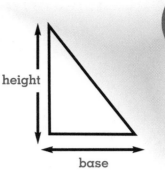

height

base

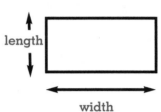

length

width

15cm

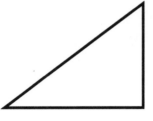

10cm

1. Area =_____ cm

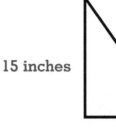

15 inches

10 inches

2. Area =_____ inches

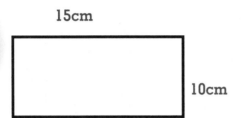

17 meters

12 meters

3. Area =_____ meters

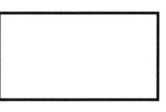

19.8mm

17.4mm

4. Area =_____ mm

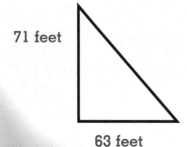

71 feet

63 feet

5. Area =_____ feet

5.5 kilometers

4.4 kilometers

6. Area =_____ kilometers

PROGRESSIVE WORDS

Can you get from the first word to the last by changing just one letter in each step?

Each word must be a real word!

BLINK

_____

_____

_____

STUCK

FAMOUS PEOPLE FACTS

Match the Facts to the Famous Person!

If you need help, use an encyclopedia or the Internet.

1. David Copperfield

2. Jimmy Carter

3. Theodor Geisel

4. Neil Armstrong

A. A navy pilot, he was commander of the Apollo 11 space flight, and became the first human being to walk on the moon on July 20, 1969. He is famous for the line, "That's one small step for man, one giant leap for mankind."

B. His real name is David Kotkin and he was born in Metuchen, New Jersey. He is famous for his illusions and magic. His most popular illusions have included making the Statue of Liberty disappear and walking through the Great Wall of China!

C. Born in 1924, he was the 39th U.S. president. His family ran a successful peanut business in Georgia. He was responsible for the Panama Treaty and for establishing peace between Israel and Egypt at Camp David. He lost his bid for a second term to Ronald Reagan in 1980.

D. An author and illustrator, his fans know and love him as Dr. Seuss. His most popular books include "Horton Hatches the Egg" (1940), "The Cat in the Hat" (1957), and "Green Eggs and Ham" (1960).

Friday

You've got a lot of living yet to do, but describe the happiest day of your life so far. What was involved? Who was involved? How did it change you?

_____

_____

_____

_____

_____

_____

_____

_____

_____

_____

_____

_____

_____

_____

_____

_____

_____

_____

WORD PUZZLE

Twisted Word Search

G	A	D	R	C	W	Z	L	N
T	R	E	E	K	F	H	J	R
O	O	S	B	M	Y	J	A	A
W	N	C	P	I	Q	L	G	U
T	E	H	U	Z	E	U	D	V
O	S	P	A	K	O	X	F	J
R	I	C	S	N	N	I	A	R
T	O	F	M	Y	T	G	N	K
X	W	S	O	E	L	U	A	Y
E	U	H	N	K	A	E	S	B
F	O	G	M	A	U	P	T	O
L	G	H	K	S	X	A	O	I
A	N	E	T	O	B	R	R	B
M	I	L	N	Y	O	A	W	Q
S	N	E	A	D	P	L	D	K
G	X	P	H	I	I	R	U	C
C	O	A	R	K	F	L	V	O
D	O	O	N	P	M	Q	L	U
G	S	B	J	S	L	C	V	A
E	R	A	W	E	A	T	M	S
A	L	X	H	I	N	A	O	D

In this word search the letter formations are "wrapped" around the boxes in four different ways. Check the examples below. Watch out. Words may be intertwined!

Words

Goose	Whale
Iguana	Deer
Snake	Elephant
Jaguar	Boar
Cobra	Tortoise
Monkey	Duck
Llama	Flamingo
Parrot	Seal

8-Letter Word
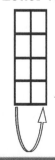

6-Letter Word
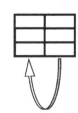

5-Letter Word
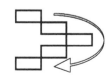

4-Letter Word

Exploring Flight:

The Great Glorious Glider Airplane Race

Adult supervision is recommended.

Thrust is what propels an airplane forward through the air. You have seen how propellers can create thrust, but there are many other ways to give an object the boost needed to achieve speed. For example, jet engines provide the great thrust needed to accelerate today's large, heavy aircraft. Solid-rocket boosters and liquid-propellant engines provide the enormous power needed to thrust space shuttles into outer space. ◆

Materials

2 sheets of 8.5 in. × 11 in.
   (21.6 cm × 27.9 cm) paper
pen or pencil

Directions

The same forces that act on real airplanes also apply to paper airplanes. To see how thrust affects the speed and distance of a craft, fold two identical copies of the same paper airplane. Follow these steps to create two Glorious Glider airplanes.

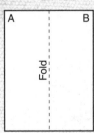

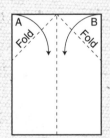

1. Fold the paper in half as shown, and then unfold.

2. Fold the top corners (A and B) to the center fold line. Note: You might want to label the corners as shown as you proceed.

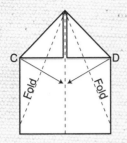

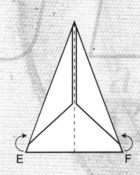

3. Fold the new corners (C and D) to the center fold line.

4. Bend the plane backward so that points E and F touch.

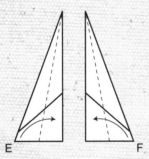

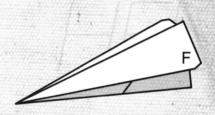

5. To create the wings, fold the plane in half, starting at the point.

6. Lift up wings E and F.

7. Repeat steps 1 through 6 to make a second plane. Give each plane a name, and mark the name on the top of the plane's wing.

8. Hold one plane in each hand between your thumb and forefinger on the bottom edge at about the midway point. Throw them at the same time in the same direction with equal amounts of force (thrust). Conduct several test flights, using the same hand to throw each plane. Launch the planes using differing amounts of thrust. Does one plane always seem to go faster and/or farther?

9. Switch planes and throw each with the alternate hand. If you are right-handed, does the plane thrown from your right hand usually go faster and/or farther? If you are left-handed, does the plane thrown from your left hand usually go faster and/or farther? Why?

More Mega Math

How many triangles add up to 8?

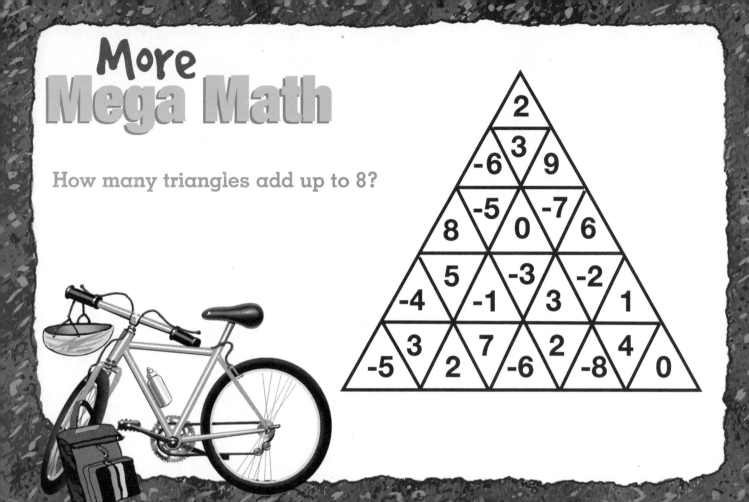

Brain Teaser

Which one doesn't belong?

cheese   rice

sponge

shoe   birthday

Fill in the Homonyms

Homonyms sound, or are spelled, the same but mean different things. Fill in the blanks below with the correct homonyms.

1 _____ have an eyelash in my _____.

2 My mother needs to go _____ the bakery to _____ a cake.

3 Did you _____ that there are _____ more tickets available?

4 My father's sister, _____ Sara, has an _____ farm.

5 _____ did you find the Halloween costume you plan to _____?

6 Sam's dad said, "_____, put on some sunblock. That _____ is really strong."

7 Did you _____ the teacher tell us to come over _____?

8 I _____ the book with the _____ cover.

Hudson's Children

CHAPTER FIVE

Terra, Trekk and Trekk's dad stopped to show their passports at the border and headed northwest on Queen's Highway 17. They made camp for the night at Lake Superior Provincial Park. Both Trekk and Terra were excited to be in Canada. "Part of it," Trekk said, "just comes from small changes, like 'Queen's Highway 17' instead of a state road, and being in a 'Provincial Park' instead of a state park."

"I know," Terra said. "It just gives me a sense of a frontier because it's so different."

"Frontier," Trekk said. "It doesn't seem too wild to me. But it is different. Even the trash barrels in the park have MNR on them."

"In the States," his dad said, "we have departments of natural resources. Here, it's the Ministry of Natural Resources. These terms are left over from the days when Canada was part of Great Britain. Still, it was the French who were here first."

"Is that why signs are in both English and French?" Trekk asked.

"Exactly. Most people of Quebec, the next province east, speak French as their first language. They care deeply about their traditions. Some have even wanted independence from Canada."

"What about here in Ontario?" Trekk wondered.

"Ontario was originally part of Quebec, though the French had the first forts here, too. Immigrants from England and the United States settled the area. There were clashes between the groups, and Ontario split off. There is still a lot of French influence, especially as you go toward Quebec."

"How do you say 'moose' in French, Dad?" Trekk asked. "I want to see a moose."

"I don't know," his dad laughed. "I don't speak French. Maybe moose," he said in a terrible accent.

"That can't be right," Trekk said, as Terra made a face. Terra and Trekk woke early the next morning. They came out of their tents and decided to explore. In the early morning quiet, Trekk heard a rustling in the brush, just over a little rise beyond the campground.

"Terra, listen!" he said softly.

"I hear it," she responded. "Sshh," she hissed as Trekk started toward the sound. As quietly as they could, they moved closer to the crunching sound.

"Maybe it's our moose," Terra whispered.

"Or a bear," Trekk said. The noise grew louder as they crawled closer. Lying flat, skin crawling, they peered cautiously over the edge of the rise. A crash of brush made Terra and Trekk jump. In a flurry of twigs and dry leaves, a grey squirrel bounded away.

Terra laughed. "Some wilderness," Trekk said disgustedly.

Monday

Activity 5

Skill: Summarizing

Write the name of the place that matches each of the following descriptions. Not all words will be used.

Chicago

Ann Arbor

Detroit

White Cloud

Milwaukee

Petoskey

Mackinaw City

Escanaba

Whitefish Point

Sault Ste. Marie

Lake Superior Provincial Park

Thunder Bay

1. Terra joins Trekk and her Uncle Phil.

_____

2. Terra breathes in "the world at its best."

_____

3. Trekk takes an unexpected swim.

_____

4. "Mighty Mac" spans the Straits.

_____

5. The travelers visit the Great Lakes Shipwreck Museum.

_____

6. The travelers cross the border.

_____

7. Trekk and Terra face a "wild animal."

_____

Math Maze

Where Do You Finish?

- Begin with "16" in the upper left-hand corner.

- Moving down or horizontally to the left or right, choose the correct path to arrive at a three-digit number whose digits are all the same.

- NOTE: You must stay on the gridlines as you move and do not backtrack.

- Each "square" is worth -8. All circled numbers are to be added.

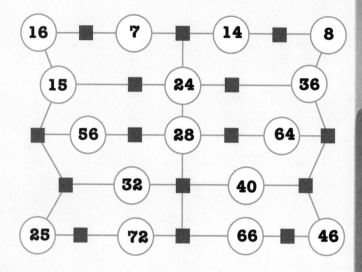

For example:
25 ■ 10 = 27 (25 - 8 = 17 + 10 = 27)

Word Games

Can you guess the relationship?

① cork   ice   boat   wood

② scorpion   wasp   jellyfish   nettles

③ John   Abraham   George   Ronald

NO BONES ABOUT IT

Match the bones to the part of the body. If you need help, use an encyclopedia or the Internet.

1. humerus

a. knee

2. femur

b. shoulder

3. ulna

c. upper arm

4. fibula

d. chest

5. sternum

e. neck

6. patella

f. lower leg

7. scapula

g. forearm

8. cervical vertebrae

h. thigh

ULTIMATE SCRAMBLE

Directions: Unscramble the letters below to form words. Unscramble the circled letters from each word to solve the riddle.

1 **netpal**

2 **ocemt**

3 **ditasroe**

4 **reemstpoah**

5 **etceslail**

Hint: *Johnny dreamed of being an astronaut. His teacher thought he was a...*

Answer:

Mega Math

Use pennies, nickels, dimes, quarters, half dollars,
and silver dollars to solve these problems.

Holly is saving money for a new soccer ball. She has saved
$55.02 so far. If she has an equal number of four different coins,
which coins does she have? How many of each?

Comparative and Superlative

Some adjectives, usually those with two or more syllables, use "more"
and "most" to form their comparative and superlative forms.
Fill in the blanks below.

	Word	Comparative	Superlative
1	horrible	_____	_____
2	generous	_____	_____
3	terrific	_____	_____
4	delicious	_____	_____
5	ridiculous	_____	_____
6	complicated	_____	_____

Thursday

Plot the Coordinates

Plot the coordinates on the graph below and label them with the correct letters. The first number tells the horizontal position (how far to the right). The second number tells the vertical position (how far up). The first one is done for you.

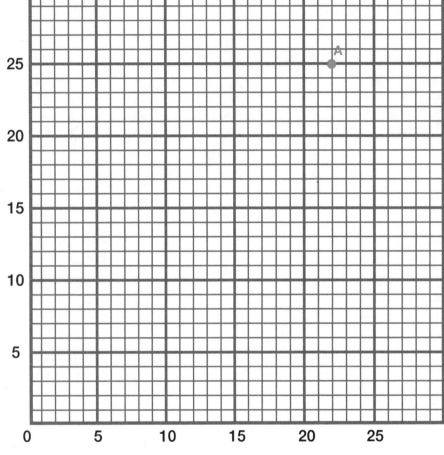

A = 22, 25	J = 14, 19	S = 3, 18
B = 7, 17	K = 4, 9	T = 10, 10
C = 1, 20	L = 24, 19	U = 11, 22
D = 25, 11	M = 2, 8	V = 13, 17
E = 17, 19	N = 9, 7	W = 8, 8
F = 8, 5	O = 13, 13	X = 9, 12
G = 4, 21	P = 12, 15	Y = 11, 25
H = 20, 10	Q = 16, 23	Z = 20, 24
I = 10, 20	R = 22, 2	

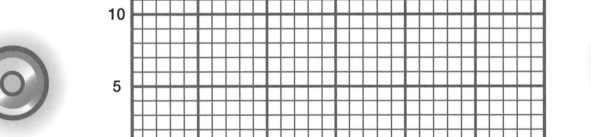

Can you get from the first word to the last by changing just one letter in each step?

Each word must be a real word!

GLASS

_____

_____

_____

_____

CROWN

FAMOUS PEOPLE FACTS

Match the Facts to the Famous Person!

If you need help, use an encyclopedia or the Internet.

1. Sandra Day O'Connor
2. Charlie Chaplin
3. Walt Disney
4. Mother Teresa

A. He was a movie animator and producer. His most famous character, Mickey Mouse, first appeared in the short animated feature "Steamboat Willie" in 1928. His biggest cartoon hits have included "Snow White and the Seven Dwarfs" (1937), "Pinocchio" (1940), "Dumbo" (1941), and "Bambi" (1942).

B. She was a Christian missionary in India. Born in Skopje, Yugoslavia, in 1910, she spent her life aiding the poor and sick. For her work she was awarded the Nobel Peace Prize in 1979.

C. She was born in El Paso, Texas, in 1930. She was elected to the Arizona state senate and to a county superior court. In 1981, she became the first woman to be appointed to the U.S. Supreme Court.

D. An actor, producer, writer and director, he was one of the all-time great silent film stars. His most well-known role was "The Little Tramp." An English citizen, he was knighted by Queen Elizabeth II in 1975 for his contributions to the arts.

Friday

A brief description of an idea for a movie, including its storyline and characters, is called a "treatment." Write a "treatment" starring yourself in a new movie. It can be an action/thriller, a drama, a horror film, or a comedy.

_____

_____

_____

_____

_____

_____

_____

_____

_____

_____

_____

_____

_____

_____

_____

_____

_____

WORD PUZZLE

Mystery Word

	A	B	C	D	E
1	C	O	W	N	A
2	L	S	I	U	B
3	M	D	T	F	T
4	I	O	P	E	G
5	E	R	C	A	B

- Use the box above to fill in the letters below.

- Each letter of the mystery word will use only one of the letters from each column below (top or bottom letter).

- Can you decipher the mystery ocean (or sea)?

D5	E1	C5	E2	D3	E1	D1
C4	B5	E1	B4	C2	A3	C1

Exploring Flight:
Drag Racing to the Ground

Adult supervision is recommended.

An opposite force—drag—is at work to spoil the power of an airplane's thrust. Drag is air resistance that pulls back and slows an aircraft. If you have ever stuck your hand out of a moving car or extended an arm to the side while riding a bike, you have experienced drag. The air against your arm and hand pulls them backward. Modern engineers strive to create aerodynamic aircraft designs that minimize drag. A heavy, bulky aircraft needs lots of thrust to overcome drag. A smoother, more streamlined craft needs less thrust to combat the drag it creates. ◆

Materials
masking tape
6 paper clips
4 clothespins
4 paper muffin liners
tape measure, yardstick, or ruler

Directions
See for yourself how drag affects the speed at which objects with different shapes fall to the ground. It would be helpful to have an observer.

1. Using a tape measure, yardstick, or ruler, mark three heights on a wall or other surface at 3 ft. (.9 m), 4 ft. (1.2 m), and 5 ft. (1.5 m). Use masking tape to mark the heights if needed.

2. Connect five paper clips into a chain as shown.

3. Connect three clothespins together as shown.

4. Simultaneously drop the five paper clips and a single paper clip from a height of 3 ft. (.9 m). Use the form below to record which hits the ground first or whether they hit the ground at approximately the same time.

5. Try dropping the paper clips in the same manner from 4 ft. (1.2 m) and 5 ft. (1.5 m). Record your results on the form.

6. Repeat the test using three clothespins and a single clothespin. Then test using three stacked muffin liners and a single muffin liner. Record your results on the form.

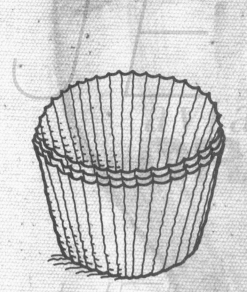

Test Results

Object	Drop Distance	Which Lands First
Paper clips	3 ft. (.9 m)	
	4 ft. (1.2 m)	
	5 ft. (1.5 m)	
Clothespins	3 ft. (.9 m)	
	4 ft. (1.2 m)	
	5 ft. (1.5 m)	
Muffin liners	3 ft. (.9 m)	
	4 ft. (1.2 m)	
	5 ft. (1.5 m)	

More Mega Math

Each of the symbols below represents a number between 1 - 10. Can you figure out which number should fill in the blank?

Converting Fractions to Decimals

1. $\frac{17}{1000}$ = _____

2. $5\frac{199}{1000}$ = _____

3. $6\frac{35}{10000}$ = _____

4. $\frac{999}{10000}$ = _____

5. $5\frac{5}{1000}$ = _____

6. $792\frac{1777}{10000}$ = _____

7. $\frac{84}{1000}$ = _____

8. $2\frac{27}{10000}$ = _____

Fantasy vs. Reality

Realistic writing is based on events that could happen.
Fantasy writing is based on events that could never happen.

Circle Fantasy or Reality for each sentence below.

1 The dog was bigger than a skyscraper.   Fantasy   Reality

2 Our football team won every game this season.   Fantasy   Reality

3 Mary's cat asked her, "When will dinner be ready?"   Fantasy   Reality

4 Sam, my brother, can fly higher than an eagle.   Fantasy   Reality

5 The doctor cured the patient.   Fantasy   Reality

6 The creepy, old house called to me.   Fantasy   Reality

7 My father is an award-winning writer.   Fantasy   Reality

8 The slimy monster slithered out of the creek and sang songs.   Fantasy   Reality

Hudson's Children

CHAPTER SIX

The three went for a swim in Lake Superior before leaving the park. None were prepared for how cold the water was. They ate lunch on the beach and felt a little foolish as they huddled in jackets while people walked past in bathing suits.

Driving northwest, they pulled off the highway briefly to see one of the most photographed sites in Ontario, the famous goose statue in Wawa. The two-ton goose had a twenty-foot wingspan. "Why did they put this here, Dad?" Trekk asked.

"When the Trans-Canadian highway went through, local businesspeople wanted something to get people to stop here."

"Why a goose?" Terra wondered.

"Well, 'Wawa' means 'Land of the Big Goose' or 'Wild Goose' in Ojibway. You know, I was wrong when I said that the French were the first to settle in Canada. Native peoples settled here centuries before Europeans came. A lot of place names around here are Ojibway, as are some that you already know, such as 'Mississippi' and 'Milwaukee.'"

"You don't know French, but you know Ojibway?" Terra asked. Her uncle grinned.

"This one I studied. The Ojibway were once one of the largest groups in North America. Some people think they migrated here from the Hudson Bay area."

"Oh," Trekk said. "I had forgotten about the Hudson part of this trip."

"Well, I hadn't," his dad said. "Though I haven't had a great idea yet."

"Don't worry," Terra said. "You will."

"Or we will," Trekk added.

As they drove on through the day, Trekk and Terra noted that there were fewer and fewer signs of human activity. "Not much out here," Trekk said.

"What are those, Uncle Phil?" Terra asked. At the side of the highway was a small road leading into the woods. Behind the trees, she could see an opening. She had seen several of these on the way.

"Those are what's left of construction camps. When they built the road, they'd clear a space to park the equipment as they went along. Let's pull in and have a look."

The truck followed the narrow entry into a sandy clearing. They drove to the edge and then circled back toward the highway. The truck's wheels began to spin. The truck slowed and then stopped.

Getting out of the truck, they noticed the wheels sinking in the sandy soil. "It's too soft," Trekk's dad said. He tried rocking the truck gently, then harder. The truck's wheels just sank deeper. The rear axles were down in the sand, and the nose pointed skyward like a sinking ship. Daylight was fading.

"Looks like we're spending the night here," Trekk's dad said. Trekk and Terra looked to the edge of the clearing. Not a sound could be heard from the road or the darkening woods.

Monday

Activity 6

Skill: Reading Comprehension

1. Why did Terra and Trekk feel foolish as they ate lunch on the beach?

   _____

   _____

2. Who are the Ojibway?

   _____

   _____

3. What does the Ojibway word "*Wawa*" mean?

   _____

   _____

4. Why was the statue of the goose built?

   _____

5. What did Trekk and Terra notice about the countryside as they traveled through the day?

   _____

6. Why were the clearings built alongside the highway?

   _____

7. Why couldn't Terra, Trekk and his dad return to the highway?

   _____

8. How will being stuck affect the trip?

   _____

Odd Number Out

Can you figure out which number doesn't belong?
Circle the correct answer.

1.   29   7   35   11   43

2.   17   19   37   18   47

3.   53   7   67   13   88

Comparative and Superlative Exceptions

Some adjectives form the comparative and superlative by making
a complete change in their form. Fill in the blanks below.

	Word	Comparative	Superlative
1	good	better	best
2	less	_____	_____
3	some	_____	_____
4	bad	_____	_____

WHO SAID IT?

Match the quotes to the people who said them. If you need help, use an encyclopedia or the Internet.

1. "I have a dream…"

a. Yogi Berra

2. "Give me liberty or give me death."

b. Benjamin Franklin

3. "That's one small step for man, one giant leap for mankind."

c. Albert Einstein

4. "Three may keep a secret, if two are dead."

d. Abraham Lincoln

5. "It ain't over 'til it's over."

e. Dr. Martin Luther King, Jr.

6. "Those who deny freedom to others, deserve it not for themselves; and, under a just God, can not long retain it."

f. John F. Kennedy

7. "Ask not what your country can do for you, but what you can do for your country."

g. Patrick Henry

8. "I think and think for months and years. Ninety-nine times the conclusion is false. The hundredth time I am right."

h. Neil Armstrong

GRID LOGIC

	Claire	Raj	Indira	Sophia	Justin	Nashville, TN	San Francisco, CA	Seattle, WA	Atlanta, GA	Honolulu, HI	April 10th	June 18th	July 12th	July 30th	August 5th
Nandi															
Bass															
Patel															
Danner															
Truscello															
April 10th															
June 18th															
July 12th															
July 30th															
August 5th															
Nashville, TN															
San Francisco, CA															
Seattle, WA															
Atlanta, GA															
Honolulu, HI															

Indira and her four friends went on a vacation this year with their parents. They all went to different places and traveled on different days. From the following clues, can you figure out each friend's full name, where they went, and when they left to begin their vacation?

1. Claire and her friend, the Bass boy, both left for their trips before the child who went to Seattle and Raj (his parents couldn't leave until later in the summer). They left after the girl who went to Nashville.

2. Indira and the Patel child did not go to a city near the ocean.

3. The girl who went to San Francisco left after the Nandi girl, but before Sophia.

4. The boy who visited Atlanta, the girl who left on July 30th, and the girl who left on July 12th, all live in the same neighborhood.

5. Sophia and the Danner girl are best of friends.

Mega Math

Can you solve the following problem? Assign different values for consonants and vowels. Can you detect a rule for solving the unknown amount?

Fall was approaching. Martine and Kevin went to buy school supplies. Together they bought:

- Backpack $22.00
- Markers $19.00
- Paints   ?

How much did the paints cost? What's the rule?

Riddles

1. I am found in the sea and on land but I do not walk or swim. I travel by foot but I am toeless. No matter where I go, I'm never far from home. What am I?

_____

2. I don't have lungs or a chest but I need air; I am not alive, but I grow; I don't have a mouth and I don't like water. What am I?

_____

3. My name means something that's used in an instrument that determines how hot you are. I'm also the name of a planet. Who am I?

_____

Thursday

Optical Illusions

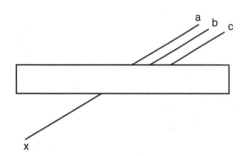

Which line is connected to line x? Line a, b or c?

Does there appear to be gray circles at the intersections of the white lines? Focus on any of the circles and they disappear!

Is the small box sitting in the corner of a wall or is it attached to a larger box?

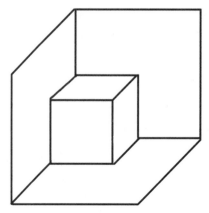

PROGRESSIVE WORDS

Can you get from the first word to the last by changing just one letter in each step?

Each word must be a real word!

PLATE

_____

_____

_____

_____

STORM

FAMOUS PEOPLE FACTS

Match the Facts to the Famous Person!

If you need help, use an encyclopedia or the Internet.

1. Benjamin Franklin
2. Elvis Aron Presley
3. Michael Jordan
4. Harry Houdini

A. This person actually had a twin brother who was stillborn. He was a singer and movie actor. Called the "King of Rock and Roll," he began singing in his church choir and won a school singing contest at the age of ten. He built a mansion called Graceland that is still a popular tourist attraction today. He died tragically at the age of 42.

B. His middle name is Jeffrey. Followers of the sport generally agree he is the greatest to ever play basketball. He has won an NCAA championship (1982), two gold medals (1984 & 1992), and six NBA titles (1991, 1992, 1993, 1996, 1997, 1998).

C. Born Ehrich Weiss in Budapest, Hungary, this person became famous for daring stunts and impossible escapes from such contraptions as locked chains, straitjackets and underwater chests. He was President of the Society of American Magicians (1917-1926).

D. A man of many skills. He was a printer, writer, scientist and statesman. He helped to establish the U.S. Post Office, the first lender library, and the University of Pennsylvania. He also invented the bifocal lens and the lightning rod.

Friday

Newsflash! You've been given the lead story assignment for your neighborhood's newspaper "Talk of the Town." Write a one page feature article on something or someone interesting that is a part of your neighborhood.

_____

_____

_____

_____

_____

_____

_____

_____

_____

_____

_____

_____

_____

_____

_____

WORD PUZZLE

Word Box

C	R	I	M	E
R				N
I				T
M				E
E	N	T	E	R

Fill in the word square above using these nine letters:

- four of the letter "O"
- two of the letter "D"
- one each of the letters "A", "I" and "S"

This is a total of 25 letters (including the letters already given). The resulting words can be read both across and down.

Exploring Flight:
Super Duper Chopper 'Copter
Adult supervision is recommended.

You have seen how drag can slow the movement of an object in flight. Notice how a bird's aerodynamic wings "slice" effortlessly through the air as it glides. Birds are shaped to minimize drag and to counter their weight as well as the pull of gravity. Gliders and machines that are designed for flight, such as helicopters and airplanes, utilize the design of a bird's wings to reduce drag and help stabilize and control flight. ◆

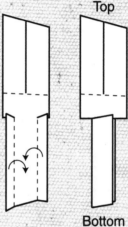

Top

Bottom

Figure 2

Materials
scissors
tape
paper clips
Manila file folder (optional)
construction paper (optional)
cereal box (optional)

Directions
Drag does not just work against pilots when they fly. They can use drag to help control the flight, such as its rate of descent, speed and stability. Create the Super Duper Chopper 'Copter and experiment with the effects of drag and weight.

1. Cut out the rectangle template on the next page. See *Figure 1*.

2. Cut along the short, horizontal, solid lines in the middle of the template. Fold the bottom flaps in along the dotted lines, and tape them to the middle section. See *Figure 2*.

3. Hold the 'copter at a height of approximately 5 ft. (1.5 m) with the bottom pointing down, and drop. Observe how the 'copter flies.

_____

_____

Figure 1

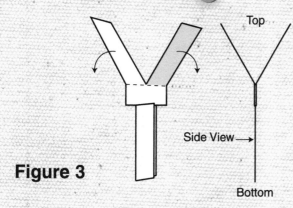

Top

Side View →

Bottom

Figure 3

4. Next, cut the vertical line on the top half of the 'copter to create helicopter blades. Bend down the blades to opposite sides along the dotted lines. Keep the blades at a slight angle. *See Figure 3.*

5. Drop the 'copter from the same height. How does it fly this time?

_____

_____

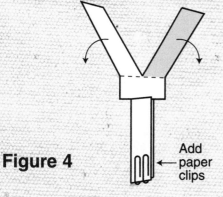

Add paper clips

Figure 4

6. Experiment by adding paper clips to the bottom of the 'copter. *See Figure 4.* How does the added weight affect the flight and why?

_____

_____

7. Create 'copters made from other materials, such as a Manila file folder, construction paper, or cereal box cardboard. Observe how different materials affect the 'copter's flight.

Top

Bottom

More Mega Math

How many squares add up to 5?

0	-3	5	-4	1	-5
6	2	1	0	-2	8
2	-3	4	3	7	-9
-1	0	-2	0	1	10
1	5	-8	9	-6	0
2	2	6	-2	7	4

Word Pictures

Can you guess what these mean?

1. PERSONALITY

2. splostace

3. READ

4. BOTTIMETLE

5. STRAWBERRY CAKE

6. TOMORROW DAY

7. LIVE LEARN

8. TUNNEL ⚪

Optical Illusions

Can you guess what these mean?

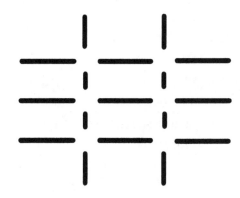

Do you see the word "Liar"? What else do you see?

Do you see circles at the line intersections? In reality, there are none!

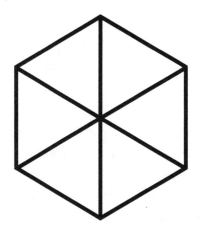

There are two objects in this figure. One is a hexagon. What is the other?

Is the card folded toward you or away from you?

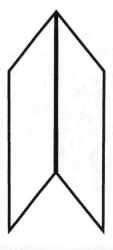

Hudson's Children

CHAPTER SEVEN

Trekk and Terra felt a little nervous that night as they set up camp. Being alone out here was different from being in an area set aside for camping.

"So, do you want to see a bear tonight, Trekk?" Terra grinned.

Trekk grinned back. "This is a good night for it. Wolves, too." That night, after letting the fire go out, Trekk and Tara stared up into the night sky. The number of stars they could see always amazed the cousins when they were far enough away from the city to see all of them. Yet, they were aware that things were different, and neither Trekk nor Terra slept well. Both woke several times in the night and listened hard.

The next morning, Trekk's dad continued trying to get the truck loose. He tried gently rocking again, first shifting into reverse, and then going forward to gain momentum. By now the truck had dug itself so far down that he made little progress. Trekk and Tara collected brush and wedged it under the tires to try to get some traction. This time the truck moved a little, but then it spewed out the branches and sank back.

Terra remembered reading about pioneer "corduroy roads" made out of logs. She and Trekk found some dead trees and used an axe to cut them. Trekk's dad dug out some more sand, trying to make the slope less steep. They carefully placed the logs near the rear wheels. Gently, Trekk's dad eased the truck onto the logs and out of the hole the tires had dug. They all cheered as the truck rose, but they soon fell into silence. No matter how gently Trekk's dad tried to drive, the truck just began sinking again.

"We might have to build this corduroy road back to the highway," Terra said. "Or at least back to where the sand was firmer."

"That could take days," Trekk wailed.

"We could do what we just did, and gain a few feet at a time," his dad said. "That would save cutting trees to build a whole road." His dad sent Trekk to the highway to watch for passing cars. Trekk waited and waited, looking up and down the empty road, but no one came. As the afternoon shadows lengthened, it became clear that they would be out here for another night. Trekk rejoined his father and cousin.

"I want to get out of here," Trekk complained.

"You wanted adventure," Terra pointed out.

"Don't remind me," Trekk said, looking down as evening closed in.

Monday

Activity 7

Skill: Predicting

Write a prediction in response to each of the following questions. Be sure to write complete sentences.

1. What would you do if you were in the same situation as Terra, Trekk and Trekk's dad?

   _____

   _____

   _____

2. Do you think the travelers will see bear, moose or wolves before they get out? Why?

   _____

   _____

3. If you had a similar adventure, would you feel nervous about spending the night in the wilderness? Why?

   _____

   _____

4. Would you have come back to the clearing, as Trekk did? Why?

   _____

   _____

5. What other problems or dangers do the travelers face as they try to free the truck?

   _____

   _____

6. How do you think they will get out of the clearing?

   _____

Math Maze

Break it in half!

- The object is to reduce your number until you arrive at a total of "16."

- Begin at the number "40" in the top left corner and choose the correct path to the bottom.

- Each time you cross a "triangle" you must divide your number by two, then proceed to add the next circled number to your total.

- You may go across or down but remember to stay on the lines.

- Also, remember that the "triangle" means that you divide your number by two (or break it in half!).

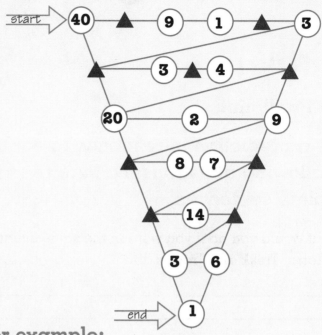

For example:
$20 \triangle 7 = 17 \ (20 \div 2 = 10 + 7 = 17)$

No Double Negatives

Never use double negatives when you write or speak. Correct the sentences below to eliminate the double negative.

1 She didn't say nothing.

_____

2 There weren't no shoes left in my size.

_____

3 He doesn't know nobody in his new school.

_____

4 Don't leave none of the milk in your glass.

_____

HELP WANTED

Match the professional titles to their area of expertise.
If you need help, use an encyclopedia or the Internet.

1. optometrist

2. botanist

3. entomologist

4. geologist

5. podiatrist

6. dermatologist

7. paleontologist

8. etymologist

a. language

b. fossils

c. skin

d. insects

e. eyes

f. feet

g. earth

h. plants

ULTIMATE SCRAMBLE

Directions: Unscramble the letters below to form words. Unscramble the circled letters from each word to solve the riddle.

1 kojer

2 flypual

3 drewpa

4 mifcseih

5 ilgegg

Hint: A sarcastic smart fellow is a...

Answer:

Mega Math

Use pennies, nickels, dimes, quarters, half dollars, and silver dollars to solve these problems.

To raise money for new uniforms the football team is selling candy. After one week they have made $22.92. There is an equal number of coins. What coins do they have? How many of each?

Find the Percent of Each Number

Convert each percent to a decimal, then multiply to solve the problems below.

Example: 6% of 32 = .06 x 32 = 1.92

1. 5% of 25 = _____
2. 16% of 26 = _____
3. 72% of 105 = _____
4. 11% of 5 = _____
5. 52% of 91 = _____
6. 33% of 99 = _____
7. 89% of 246 = _____
8. 20% of 10 = _____

Thursday

Read the Graph

Annual Grocery Spending for Jones Family

Examine the graph to answer the questions below.

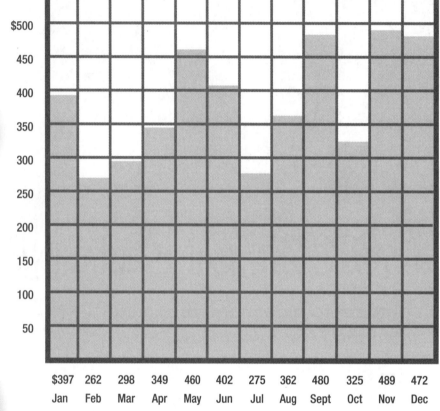

$397	262	298	349	460	402	275	362	480	325	489	472
Jan	Feb	Mar	Apr	May	Jun	Jul	Aug	Sept	Oct	Nov	Dec

1. In what month did the Jones family spend the most money?

_____

2. In what month did the Jones family spend the least money?

_____

3. What is the difference between the greatest and least amount of spending?

_____

4. What is the monthly spending average? Remember, to calculate average you add the totals for each month and divide by the total number of months.

_____

Can you get from the first word to the last by changing just one letter in each step?

Each word must be a real word!

CRAVE

_____

_____

_____

GLIDE

FAMOUS PEOPLE FACTS

Match the Facts to the Famous Person!

If you need help, use an encyclopedia or the Internet.

1. Franklin Delano Roosevelt

2. Bill Cosby

3. George Washington Carver

4. Larry Joe Bird

A. Born into slavery sometime around 1861, he studied agriculture at Iowa State University. Later, at the Tuskegee Institute, he investigated ways to replenish soils by rotating crops. He discovered hundreds of uses for the peanut, including peanut butter!

B. Our country's 32nd president. He took office on the heels of the Great Depression. Many important programs were implemented during his New Deal campaign, including the Tennessee Valley Authority, the Securities and Exchange Commission, and Social Security. He is the only president to serve four terms! He also suffered from a bout with polio and was confined to a wheelchair.

C. Born in French Lick, Indiana, he played college basketball for Indiana State University against Earvin "Magic" Johnson and Michigan State University in the 1979 NCAA championship game. ISU lost, but the rivalry with Johnson was just beginning. Drafted by the Boston Celtics, he won NBA championships in 1981, 1984 and 1986. He was named league MVP three times and played on the 1992 "dream team" alongside Johnson.

D. As a comedian, he has been a part of American mainstream for decades. He has hosted several shows including the animated series Fat Albert. His most famous character was the lovable doctor Cliff Huxtable.

Friday

What do you think you will have done in a year from now? What places will you have visited? What new friends might you make? How much will you have grown? How well will you have done in the upcoming school year?

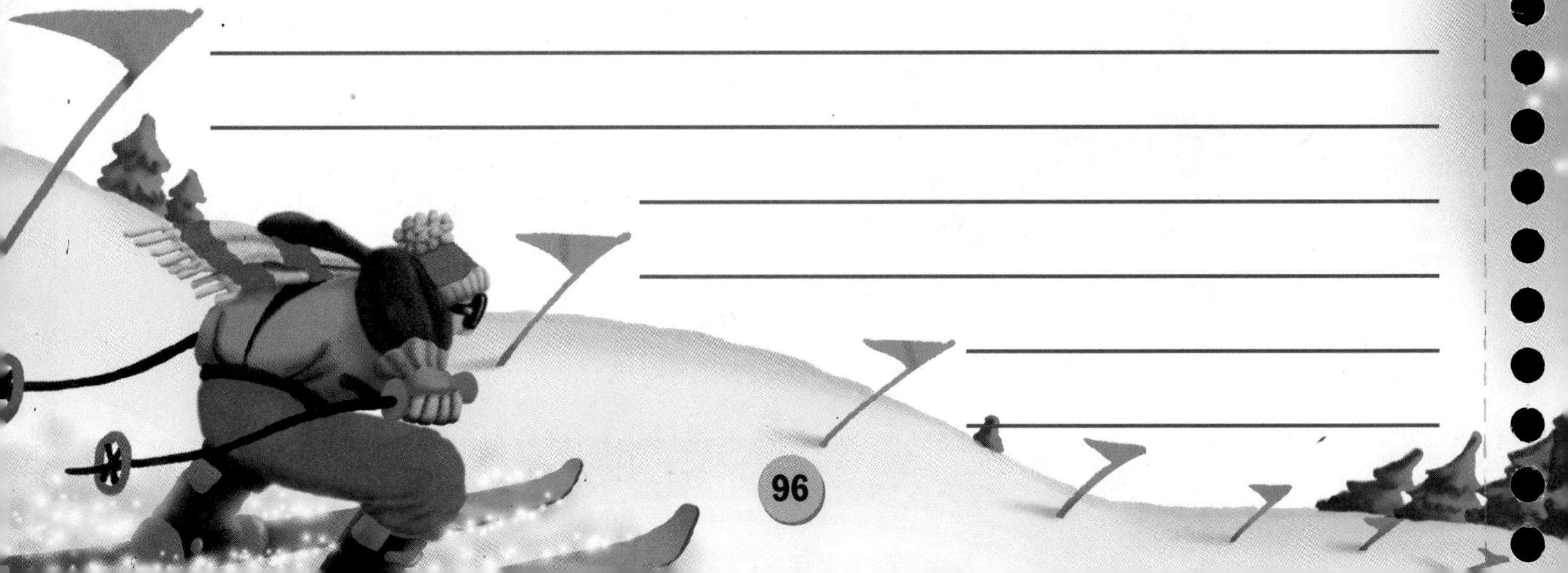

_____

_____

_____

_____

_____

_____

_____

_____

_____

_____

_____

_____

_____

_____

_____

_____

WORD PUZZLE

Mystery Word

	A	B	C	D	E
1	B	X	F	C	O
2	L	S	K	S	G
3	E	A	R	P	L
4	H	C	I	N	D
5	T	Y	U	E	B

- Use the box above to fill in the letters below.

- Each letter of the mystery word will use only one of the letters from each column below (top or bottom letter).

- Can you decipher the mystery instrument?

D2	D5	B4	D4	A3	D3
A5	E1	D4	D1	B3	C3

Exploring Flight:

Building a Daring Dart Flier

Adult supervision is recommended.

In order for an airplane to fly, it must perfectly balance the four forces of flight (weight, lift, thrust, and drag), which simultaneously act on it in flight. Not only must it stay in the air, it also must be stable and easily controlled by the pilot. You can learn more about the four forces of flight and how they interact by seeing the forces at work on a sophisticated paper airplane. ◆

Materials

8.5 in. × 11 in.
   (21.6 cm × 27.9 cm) paper
scissors
ruler
pencil

Directions

Create your own Daring Dart Flier by following these directions:

1. Fold a sheet of paper in half lengthwise, and then unfold it.

2. Fold the top corners so that they line up with the center fold.

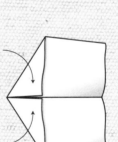

3. Fold the new corners diagonally so that they line up with the center fold. You should end up with a triangle shape.

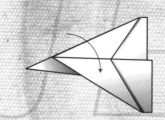

4. Fold the plane in half.

5. Fold the wings down, starting about 2.5 in. (6.4 cm) from the nose point.

6. Fold the wings all the way up again. Make a 1.5 in. (3.8 cm) cut where the wings come to a horizontal line at the top. This will become the vertical tail wing.

7. Hold the plane by its body in flying position with the wings flared out above your fingers horizontally. Make a 1.25 in. (3.2 cm) cut on the original center fold at the bottom of the plane's body. These cuts will create the engines on both sides of the plane.

8. Hold the plane so that you are looking at its side. Make a vertical cut at a 90-degree angle to the cut in step 7. Stop the cut where the wings fold.

9. Using a pencil, carefully roll up and curl the engine flaps on both sides of the plane. One engine will be below each wing.

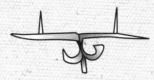

10. Hold the plane in flying position. Fold up the tail wing flaps vertically so that they are parallel to each other.

Now it is time to have fun! Let your Daring Dart Flier soar!

More Mega Math

Each of the symbols represents a number between 1 - 10. Can you figure out which number should fill in the blank?

 = _____

Brain Teaser

Can you identify these objects?

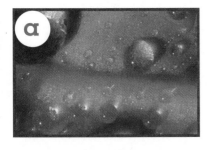

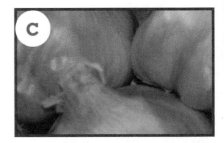

_____

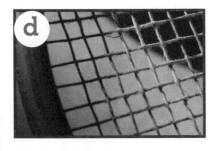

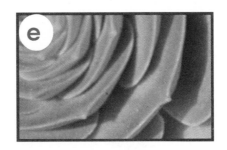

_____

100

Subject and Predicate

A sentence has two parts—a subject and a predicate.

The predicate is the part that says something about the subject.

Circle the predicate in each sentence below.

1. My math book is so heavy.

2. The macaroni and cheese tastes salty.

3. Sara fell on the playground.

4. Bill learned to water ski last summer.

5. Mimi's sunglasses are purple with silver sequins.

6. I baked a chocolate cake today.

7. My dad's car is being repaired.

8. The towel is still wet.

9. I have sand between my toes.

10. Harold played with his nephews.

Hudson's Children

CHAPTER EIGHT

Early the next morning, Terra, Trekk and Trekk's dad went back to work moving the logs, moving the truck, and then repeating the whole process. Trekk could tell that his father was getting concerned. They worked carefully. Trekk's dad shut the truck off and set the brake when they were moving logs, and Trekk and Terra stayed clear whenever the truck moved. The procedure went slowly.

About noon a huge truck roared into the clearing. The three stood and stared as a rough-looking man got down from the driver's seat and walked over.

"'Allo," he said. "I am René. Are you stuck?" The big man spoke with a thick French accent that Terra and Trekk had difficulty understanding. He offered to help, though, and Terra could see that her uncle was glad and relieved.

René first tried driving the truck out himself, but his luck was no better than Trekk's dad's had been. Then Trekk's dad gently drove the

truck while René pushed forward and up to keep the wheels from digging in. That didn't work either. "*Quatre*," René grunted. "You need four-wheel drive."

Finally, the big man searched his truck and returned with a long chain. Keeping his own truck on firm ground, he attached the chain to both vehicles. Then he backed almost all the way to the highway, pulling the smaller truck as he went. They were free! Terra, Trekk and Trekk's dad did their best to express their gratitude. They could tell that René understood their English a lot better than they did his French. Finally René waved his hands.

"Do you have anything to drink?" he said. Terra looked at her uncle.

"Uh, just a little soda," he said slowly.

"*Bon*," René said. "Good." They sat and poured a soda into four cups. René made some sort of a toast in French, and then they drank. René laughed, and the others laughed, too. Terra asked him the French words for some common objects.

"Moose," Trekk finally said. "What is moose?"

"Mooooose," René said. Trekk looked at Terra. Could he really be making the same stupid joke as Dad? René laughed. "*Élan*," he said. He put his hands up to his head like antlers. "*Élan*."

After shaking hands with them all, René jumped into his big truck and drove away. The campers piled into their truck.

"Interesting man," Trekk's dad said, glancing at the dashboard.

"Hope we make it to a gas station after all this," he added.

"You're kidding, right?" Trekk asked.

"I wish I were," his father answered.

Monday

Activity 8

Skill: Nouns

Across

1. René spoke with this type of an accent.

2. The condition of the campers; rhymes with 2 Down

3. They toasted with this beverage.

4. Ribbed fabric; with 4 Down, a pioneer "highway"

5. _____, a moose

Down

1. What spun into the soft surface

2. Campers' vehicle

3. What the vehicle was stuck in

4. With 4 Across, a pioneer "highway"

5. The man who rescued the campers

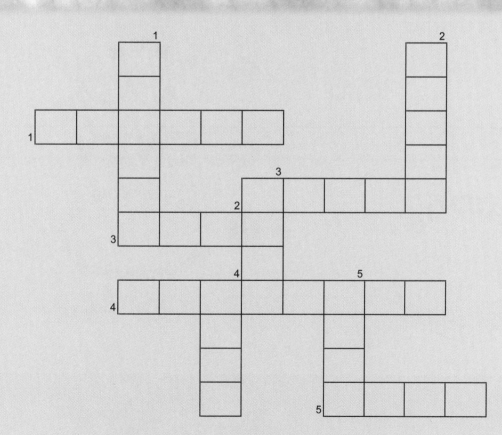

Odd Number Out

Can you figure out which number doesn't belong? Circle the correct answer.

1.   82   9   126   45   27

2.   8   96   48   12   72

3.   72   36   15   6   54

Word Pictures

Can you guess what these mean?

A. SCOTCH

B. MILK

C. BRIDGE water

D.

E. WALKING

F. ENVY

G. SOUNDSOUNDSOUNDSOUNDSOUNDSOUNDSOUNDSOUND

H. PLAY PLAY

AND YOUR NAME IS?

Match the presidents with their first and middle names.
If you need help, use an encyclopedia or the Internet.

1. Ford

2. Kennedy

3. Bush

4. Clinton

5. Carter

6. Reagan

7. Johnson

8. Nixon

a. James Earl

b. Ronald Wilson

c. Lyndon Baines

d. George Herbert Walker

e. Gerald Rudolph

f. John Fitzgerald

g. Richard Milhous

h. William Jefferson

PHOTO MATCH

Match the photo to the name of the landmark. If you need help, use an encyclopedia or the the Internet.

 a

 b

 c

 d

 e

 f

 g

 h

 i

 j

 k

 l

_____ 1. Great Wall of China

_____ 2. Stonehenge, England

_____ 3. Colosseum, Rome

_____ 4. Eiffel Tower, Paris

_____ 5. Parthenon, Athens

_____ 6. Leaning Tower of Pisa, Italy

_____ 7. Gaza Pyramids, Egypt

_____ 8. Canals of Venice

_____ 9. Aztec Ruins

_____ 10. Statue of Liberty, New York City

_____ 11. Ayers Rock, Australia

_____ 12. St. Peter's Basilica, Vatican

Mega Math

Can you solve the following problem? Think about the number of vowels and consonants in each word. Can you detect a rule for solving the unknown amount?

Andy is going camping this weekend. He went to the sporting goods store for supplies. He bought:

- Granola $12.00
- Batteries $20.00
- Sleeping Bag   ?

How much did the sleeping bag cost? What's the rule?

Riddles

1. The first half of me is a popular woman's name. The last half of me is the opposite of sea. There are 49 others like me. What am I?

_____

2. I run, but I never walk. I have a mouth, but I never talk. I have a head, but I never cry. I have a bed, but I never lie. What am I?

_____

3. I am round on both ends and high in the middle. I have two friends that have the same first initial. What state am I?

_____

4. I am the beginning of eternity and the end of time and space, the beginning of every end and the end of every place. What am I?

_____

Estimation

Round the numbers in the equations to the nearest hundred and estimate the answer.

Example:
```
    482          500
  x 211        x 200
              100,000 Estimate
```

1
```
  114  ⟶  _____
x 912
```

5
```
  633  ⟶  _____
x 747
```

2
```
  452  ⟶  _____
x 512
```

6
```
  299  ⟶  _____
x 199
```

3
```
   75  ⟶  _____
x 142
```

7
```
  387  ⟶  _____
x 439
```

4
```
  551  ⟶  _____
x 942
```

8
```
  791  ⟶  _____
x 829
```

PROGRESSIVE WORDS

Can you get from the first word to the last by changing just one letter in each step?

Each word must be a real word!

HASTE

_____

_____

_____

PETTY

FAMOUS PEOPLE FACTS

Match the Facts to the Famous Person!

If you need help, use an encyclopedia or the Internet.

1. Dr. Martin Luther King, Jr.

2. George Herman Ruth

3. Napoleon Bonaparte

4. Mohandas Gandhi

A. A nationalist leader in India, he studied law in London before returning home to fight for Indian independence. He endorsed nonviolence as a means of protest. He was arrested several times for conspiracy. Due, in part, to his efforts India achieved independence in 1947. Tragically, a Hindu fanatic assassinated him the next year.

B. A brilliant French general, he conquered much of continental Europe. He attempted an invasion of Russia but his troops were turned back by the raging Russian winter. Ultimately, after a final defeat at Waterloo, he was banished to St. Helena where he eventually died.

C. Known simply as Babe, he is one of baseball's all-time greatest players, and one of America's most popular athletes ever. He began his career in Boston as a pitcher and was eventually traded to New York where he played outfield from 1920 to 1935. He was elected to the Hall of Fame in 1936. Hank Aaron eclipsed his homerun record of 714 in 1974.

D. A Baptist minister and civil rights leader, he advocated nonviolence to achieve the goals of equality and nonsegregation. His most famous speech took place on the steps of the Lincoln Memorial in Washington, D.C., when he uttered the words "I have a dream." He won the Nobel Peace Prize in 1964. His life was cut short by an assassin's bullet in 1968.

109

Friday

Hooray! You just won a million bucks in the lottery! Instead of receiving your winnings in one lump sum, it will be evenly divided over four years. ($250,000 a year.) Describe how you would spend your money for four different years.

_____

_____

_____

_____

_____

_____

_____

_____

_____

_____

_____

_____

_____

_____

_____

_____

_____

WORD PUZZLE

Twisted Word Search

E	L	K	M	C	Q	V	T	I
B	A	W	I	D	K	U	O	A
N	R	H	A	Y	O	E	N	S
I	C	E	B	P	G	O	N	A
D	L	H	O	M	A	T	T	F
J	E	S	I	U	K	S	A	R
Q	E	E	B	L	M	T	Y	G
G	S	S	P	R	U	H	O	O
X	G	E	C	Z	I	N	G	R
I	V	A	F	B	D	E	E	U
K	F	T	D	I	Y	J	R	W
E	A	B	U	Q	S	L	D	T
C	S	R	N	R	E	H	U	O
B	E	A	K	C	O	G	S	P
R	A	E	U	D	K	W	M	U
Z	E	F	Y	O	Q	I	X	C
A	G	G	O	S	N	M	E	R
P	L	C	D	R	U	V	A	S
I	S	O	Y	L	W	G	R	J
O	O	P	V	H	E	D	T	U
N	U	E	I	M	S	S	W	O

In this word search the letter formations are "wrapped" around the boxes in four different ways. Check the examples below. Watch out. Words may be intertwined!

Words

Noodles	Pasta
Catfish	Sugar
Cookies	Bread
Chicken	Sauce
Yogurt	Tuna
Turkey	Soup
Cheese	Milk
Cereal	Eggs

7-Letter Word

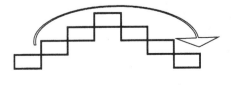

6-Letter Word

5-Letter Word

4-Letter Word

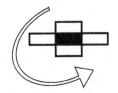

111

Exploring Flight:

Make a Kite

Adult supervision is recommended.

The history of flight spans hundreds of years, starting in approximately 400 b.c. when the Chinese invented the first kites. Since then, humankind has been fascinated with the dream of soaring like a bird in the sky. Inventors through the ages have experimented with flight, studying kites, hot air balloons, and even paper airplanes. By comparing different aircraft designs and testing them in flight, modern scientists and engineers have created amazing aerodynamic shapes that slice through the air at unbelievable speeds.◆

Materials
ruler
pen
2 plastic straws or small sticks
tape (masking tape or invisible tape)
wax paper or plastic wrap
safety pin
fishing line
8.5 in. × 11 in. (21.6 cm × 27.9 cm) paper
colored markers (optional)

Directions
Create a kite in seven simple steps. When you have finished, fly your kite in an open area, free of trees and power lines. Be sure to wait for a windy day!

1. Use a ruler to divide your straws into thirds. You can use a pen to draw lines to mark your measurements. Cut one-third off one of the straws, and throw this piece away.

2. To create your kite's frame, place the newly cut straw approximately one-third of the way down from the top of the uncut straw. Tape the two straws together.

3. Have an adult help you unclasp a safety pin. With the sharp, open end of the pin, poke a hole through the width of the top straw, as close to the top of it as you can. Also do this for the bottom and side straws of the kite's frame.

4. Thread the fishing line through one of the holes, and make a knot to secure the end. Moving along the kite's perimeter, continue threading the fishing line through the holes you made in step 3. Loop the fishing line through the first hole and tie a knot.

5. Place a piece of wax paper or plastic wrap on a flat surface, and lay your kite frame on top. Cut the wax paper around the kite's frame so that the paper is slightly larger than the kite frame. Tape the paper to the outer fishing line along your kite frame. Slightly bend down the smaller straw.

6. Cut a piece of paper twice the length of your kite and 1 in. (2.5 cm) in width. Attach this tail to the bottom of your kite. If you wish, decorate the tail with markers to personalize your kite.

7. Attach the fishing line needed to fly your kite by poking a small hole through the paper at the point where the straws intersect. Tie a knot at the end of the fishing line to give you something to hold on to.

More Mega Math

How many triangles add up to 11?

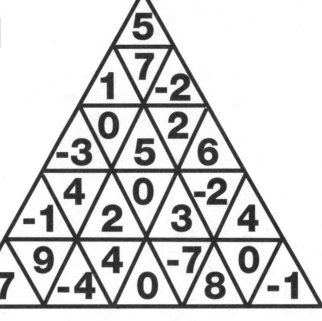

Brain Teaser

Which one doesn't belong?

UNE   AY

ARCH

EAT   ULY

Division of Fractions

To divide fractions, multiply by a reciprocal, then reduce the fraction to get the answer.

Example: $\dfrac{2}{5} \div \dfrac{9}{10} = \dfrac{2}{5} \times \dfrac{10}{9} = \dfrac{20}{45} = \dfrac{4}{9}$

1 $\dfrac{1}{3} \div \dfrac{2}{3} =$

2 $\dfrac{8}{9} \div \dfrac{5}{7} =$

3 $\dfrac{1}{2} \div \dfrac{5}{6} =$

4 $\dfrac{4}{5} \div \dfrac{3}{7} =$

5 $\dfrac{7}{10} \div \dfrac{1}{4} =$

6 $\dfrac{7}{20} \div \dfrac{1}{5} =$

7 $\dfrac{9}{11} \div \dfrac{1}{11} =$

8 $\dfrac{5}{8} \div \dfrac{3}{4} =$

Hudson's Children

CHAPTER NINE

With the gas gauge nearing *E*, Trekk's dad told stories and jokes, but the cousins could see him glance often at the sinking pointer. They breathed a sigh of relief when they made it to Hornepayne for gasoline and supplies. Trekk watched the pump run up some amazing numbers before he realized that fuel here was measured in liters, not gallons. Trekk's dad handed him some Canadian bills. "You go and pay."

"A dollar is a dollar, anyway," Trekk said.

"Not quite. Canadian and U.S. currency aren't worth the same amount. Right now, if you exchange ten U.S. dollars, you'll get about fifteen Canadian dollars. The difference depends on the exchange rate, which changes from time to time. Most places accept U.S. dollars, so you have to pay attention to the value."

Refueled and resupplied, the travelers drove on through Hearst and Kapuskasing, hoping to camp that night in René Brunelle Provincial Park. The day was overcast and they thought it might rain, so they made the best time they could. Suddenly Terra yelled, "Stop!"

"What's the matter?" Trekk said. His dad slowed the truck. Terra pointed to a seven-foot-high creature standing at the edge of the woods. "Moose," Trekk breathed.

"*Élan*," Terra whispered. The moose was huge, even from this distance.

"Must be a cow," Trekk's dad said softly. "No antlers."

"Don't bulls lose their antlers sometimes?" Trekk asked.

"In winter," his dad said. "By now they'd be growing back nicely."

"It's graceful somehow," Terra said, "and beautiful."

There was a motion behind the moose, and the cow turned. As she did, they got a glimpse of another, smaller moose just behind. Then in the blink of an eye, both were gone.

"She had a calf with her," Terra said.

"She'll keep it until it's about a year old and then send it on its way. Moose stay pretty solitary except for mating and calf-raising," Trekk's dad said.

It rained the rest of the way to the park, stopping just as they arrived. Hordes of mosquitoes followed and attacked while they set up camp.

"Yipe," Trekk said, "these things are as big as sparrows."

"No, hawks," Terra said, slapping for the hundredth time. It was unbearable. Their repellent didn't do much good. Finally, they fled to the truck, leaving most of their things outside. They had cold beans for dinner and shoved their gear around so that they could fit their sleeping bags on the truck bed.

After sleeping poorly in the cramped truck, they were awakened by loud noises. Trekk tried to see out the truck's rear window. Bulky shapes were moving outside. Someone was stealing their supplies!

Monday

Activity 9

Skill: Vocabulary

Choose the best meaning for each boldfaced word. Circle the letter next to your choice.

1. Canadian and U.S. **currency** aren't worth the same amount.
   a. numbers
   b. fuel
   c. values
   d. money

2. The day was **overcast**.
   a. troubled
   b. cloudy
   c. forgotten
   d. far away

3. They got a **glimpse** of another, smaller moose.
   a. comparison
   b. quick look
   c. noise
   d. scary sight

4. Moose stay pretty **solitary** except for mating and calf-raising.
   a. dangerous
   b. alone
   c. heavy
   d. silent

5. They were attacked by **hordes** of mosquitoes as they set up camp.
   a. sounds
   b. attacks
   c. mobs
   d. stingers

	Dawn	Lucas	Estaban	Michael	Emma	Metalheads	Stonestown Symphony	Wild Yahoos	Backyard Blues Band	Country Kickin'	Monday	Wednesday	Thursday	Friday	Saturday
Montgomery															
Hawthorne															
Guerro															
Juarez															
Chen															
Monday															
Wednesday															
Thursday															
Friday															
Saturday															
Metalheads															
Stonestown Symphony															
Wild Yahoos															
Backyard Blues Band															
Country Kickin'															

For examples and instructions on how to complete Grid Logic, see the last page of the book.

Five friends went to concerts this past week. Because they all have different tastes in music, they decided to go to five different concerts. All of the concerts were on different days. From the following clues, can you determine each child's full name, the name of the concert they attended, and the day on which the concert was held?

1. Estaban and his friend, the Montgomery girl, both went to concerts before Thursday.

2. The Chen boy saw the Metalheads later in the week than Michael saw his concert.

3. Country Kickin' played a concert earlier in the week than the Wild Yahoos, who Dawn saw in concert.

4. The Hawthorne girl, Dawn, and the child who went to Friday's concert all ride the same bus to school.

5. Backyard Blues Band played on Thursday, three days after the Guerro child went to his concert.

6. Estaban saw his concert before the Chen child and five days before the girl who saw Stonestown Symphony.

TAKE ME TO YOUR LEADER

Match the planets to their descriptions. If you need help, use an encyclopedia or the Internet.

1. Mercury

2. Jupiter

3. Pluto

4. Venus

5. Saturn

6. Mars

7. Uranus

8. Neptune

a. The God of War, Red Planet

b. The Magician, father of Saturn

c. Goddess of Love and Beauty, the "morning star"

d. God of Agriculture, ringed planet

e. God of the Underworld, not a dog

f. Winged Messenger of the gods

g. God of the Sea, in Greek it's Poseidon

h. King of the gods, Great Red Spot

ULTIMATE SCRAMBLE

Directions: Unscramble the letters below to form words. Unscramble the circled letters from each word to solve the riddle.

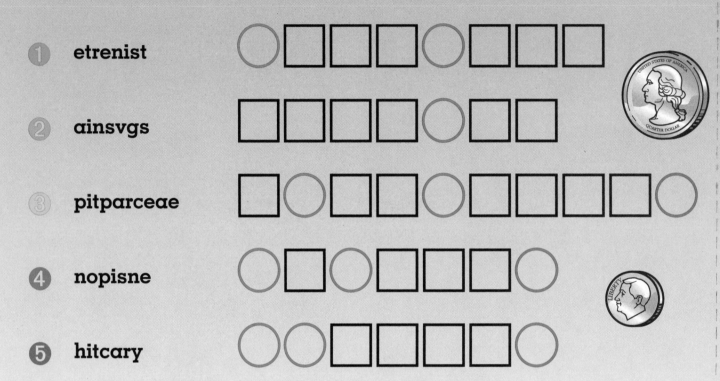

1 etrenist

2 ainsvgs

3 pitparceae

4 nopisne

5 hitcary

Hint: Suzie enjoyed squeezing cents.
She was a real...

Answer:

Mega Math

Use $1 bills, $5 bills, $10 bills, $20 bills and
$50 bills to solve this problem.

James was saving his money to buy a new pair of skis.
So far he has saved $340.00 made up of an equal
number of four different bills. Which four bills did he
have? How many of each?

Riddles

1. I am at my peak when I am round, but I am often seen in
other shapes. A man whose last name means "powerful
bicep" was the first human to walk on me. I come out at
night but sometimes you may catch a glimpse of me in
the daytime. What am I?

   _____

2. I am weightless and can be seen. When I am put in a
barrel I make it lighter. What am I?

   _____

Thursday

Place Value with Decimals

Record each number on the place value chart.
The first one is done for you.

Hundreds	Tens	Ones	And	Tenths	Hundredths	Thousandths
1. 6	4	9	•	6	9	2
2.			•			
3.			•			
4.			•			
5.			•			
6.			•			

1 six hundred forty-nine **and** six hundred ninety-two thousandths

2 fifty-one and five thousandths

3 seven hundred thirty-three and thirty-four hundredths

4 four hundred eighty-four and five hundred eleven thousandths

5 eight hundred one and two tenths

6 five hundred sixty-six and two hundred thirteen thousandths

PROGRESSIVE WORDS

Can you get from the first word to the last by changing just one letter in each step?

Each word must be a real word!

RIPEN

_____

_____

_____

_____

LONER

FAMOUS PEOPLE FACTS

Match the Facts to the Famous Person!

If you need help, use an encyclopedia or the Internet.

1. Judy Garland
2. Nicolaus Copernicus
3. Cleopatra
4. Charles Darwin

A. Queen of Egypt and daughter of the Ptolemy family. She was shrewd, resourceful and seductive. She used her relationships with Julius Caesar and Marc Antony, both prominent Romans, to secure her own throne in Egypt. After Antony's troops were routed at Actium she committed suicide to prevent being captured by Octavian.

B. Born in Grand Rapids, Minnesota, in 1922, she entered show business with her sisters in a vaudeville act. Her best known role was Dorothy in "The Wizard of Oz" (1939). She is the mother of Liza Minelli and she died in 1969.

C. Aboard the HMS Beagle he toured the South Pacific as a naturalist observing different species and climates. Several years later he published a revolutionary essay "On the Origin of Species" (1859) in which he defended the ideas of evolution and natural selection. He also authored "The Descent of Man" (1871), which proposes our descent from the apes.

D. Born in Poland, he is considered the founder of modern astronomy. In his own time, however, he was at the center of controversy for a paper he published titled "On the Revolutions of the Celestial Spheres" (1543). In it, he suggested that the earth is not the center of the universe—as taught by religious doctrine—but rather the earth rotates on its axis and revolves around the sun.

Friday

Surprise! You just won a gift certificate for a brand new Apricot computer. The computer company will design it to fit your specific needs. Describe everything you want your computer to do.

_____

_____

_____

_____

_____

_____

_____

_____

_____

_____

_____

_____

_____

_____

_____

_____

_____

Mystery Word

	A	B	C	D	E
1	N	I	K	U	D
2	G	E	T	L	F
3	O	S	E	X	C
4	Y	L	P	W	O
5	M	H	C	R	A

- Use the box above to fill in the letters below.

- Each letter of the mystery word will use only one of the letters from each column below (top or bottom letter).

- Can you decipher the mystery place?

A4	B2	D5	B4	B3	B5	A5	C2	A2	B2
A5	C2	B4	D1	E4	D4	B3	E4	D5	D3

Exploring Flight:

Jet Flier Showdown

Adult supervision is recommended.

For years, engineers and aviators have used flight simulators and models to help refine air travel and improve safety. Researchers closely study how even slight changes to an aircraft's design and materials can influence how it handles and maneuvers in the air. ◆

Materials

8.5 in. × 11 in.
  (21.6 cm × 27.9 cm)
  copier or printer paper

construction paper
  (or other heavyweight paper)

glue

scissors

onion, parchment, or wax paper, cut to 8.5 in. × 11 in.
  (21.6 cm × 27.9 cm) size
  (optional)

tape

Directions

See how the material used to make a Jet Flier can influence how it flies. First, fold two versions of the jet: one using regular-weight copier paper and the other using construction paper or other heavyweight paper. Conduct five test flights for each plane, and record each flight's speed, direction, and distance.

1. As you have done with previous paper planes, fold the paper in half, open it, and fold down the top corners to meet the center fold.

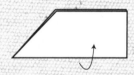

2. Fold the paper in half. The corners should be inside the fold.

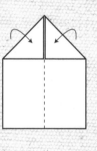

3. Fold down first one side and then the other as shown. Line up the slanted edges to create a pointed nose.

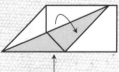

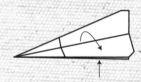

4. Create wings by folding each side again, lining each up with the bottom as shown.

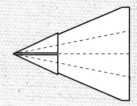

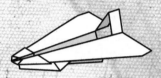

5. Unfold the jet so that it looks like this.

6. Fold the pointed nose tip down so that it meets the overlap. Now the jet has a squared-off nose.

7. Refold the paper in half with the folded nose tip inside. Tape the nose together. Mark a point about 1 in. (2.5 cm) from the back edge of the jet, and cut a vertical line up to the wing fold. This will create a tail.

8. Push the tail you cut in step 7 up through the plane so that it sticks above the plane. Mold it into a triangle shape as shown. Spread the wings slightly.

9. Experiment by adding more weight to the heavier plane. Spread glue on its wings. Let it dry, and then conduct more flight tests. How does the added weight affect how this jet flies? How might using very light, thin paper affect a jet's flight? See for yourself by folding a Jet Flier, using onion, parchment, or wax paper.

More Mega Math

Each of the symbols represents a number between 1 - 10. Can you figure out which number should fill in the blank?

△△△△■■■ = ●●●

●●■■ = △△△△△△△

△■● = _____

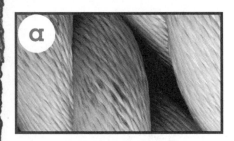

Brain Teaser

Can you identify these objects?

a _____

b _____

c _____

d _____

e _____

f _____

128

Math Quiz

Select the correct answer for each problem.

1 Which equation equals 60?

A. 5 x (10 x 2)

B. (12 x 4) − 6

C. (8 + 4) x 5

D. 6 x (12 ÷ 4)

2 Which fraction is equivalent to $\frac{2}{3}$?

A. $\frac{16}{19}$

B. $\frac{8}{12}$

C. $\frac{5}{6}$

D. $\frac{6}{14}$

3 Which decimal is equivalent to $\frac{82}{10,000}$?

A. .0082

B. .082

C. .82

D. .00082

4 What number represents the shaded figures below?

A. $1\frac{1}{3}$

B. $1\frac{1}{2}$

C. $1\frac{5}{9}$

D. $\frac{15}{9}$

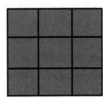
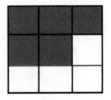

Hudson's Children

CHAPTER TEN

Terra fumbled around for a flashlight. Her uncle and Trekk crawled over each other, trying to get a better look at what was happening outside. Finally Terra found the light, turned it on, and aimed it through the window. "Bears!" Trekk shouted. Attracted by what the campers had left outside, the bears were trashing the camp. Trekk's dad took the light and lifted the rear window so he could see better. There appeared to be three of them, possibly a mother and two cubs. The bears made no effort to flee. "Shoo!" Trekk's dad yelled, and waved the beam over their faces.

"Go!" shouted Trekk. One bear half rose to look in the direction of the noise, but the light didn't seem to bother any of them.

"Shoo!" Trekk's dad yelled even louder. He stuck his arm out the rear window and pounded on the tailgate of the truck. "Get out of here!" Suddenly there was a loud metallic bang, and the whole truck shook. Terra and Trekk fell, and Trekk's dad dropped the flashlight out and let go

of the window at the same time. One of the bears hit the truck. They could hear the bear scratch the side of the bed and then hit it again. For a moment, the frightened trio thought the bears were trying to get inside. The three cowered in the truck's darkness. There was nothing to be done. After a while, it grew completely silent. They strained their eyes looking and saw nothing, but no one was tempted to go out to retrieve the flashlight, let alone look for bears.

In the gray light of dawn, the campers checked the damage. Everything in the cooler was gone or ruined. The cooler itself was destroyed, and the water jug was punctured. The side of the truck had a small dent, and there were scratches on the bed rail. "I guess I'll owe Jim some repair costs," Trekk's dad said. "Let's get this mess cleaned up before the bugs find us."

"Too late," Trekk said. "The mosquito squadron has located its target." They worked quickly to pick up the campsite, hurried by the whine of insect wings. There was nothing to do but resupply.

"We can go on to Cochrane," Trekk's dad said. "That's it anyway. There are no more roads from there. We have to go north another way."

Visions of dogsleds danced in Trekk's head, but it was July. "So now what?"

"Polar Bear Express," his dad said.

"The what?" Terra asked.

"The Polar Bear Express," her uncle replied.

"Thank you," Terra said as she stuffed the useless water jug into a trash bag, "but I've had enough bears for now."

The way north was by rail.

Monday

Activity 10

Skill: Compound Sentences

Write a sentence to answer each
of the following questions.

1. What did Terra do when she found the flashlight?

   _____

   _____

   _____

2. What did Trekk's dad do first when he took the flashlight?

   _____

   _____

3. How did Trekk's dad try to scare off the bears?

   _____

   _____

4. How did the bears react to Trekk's dad pounding on the truck?

   _____

   _____

5. What was the condition of the truck in the morning?

   _____

   _____

6. What was the condition of their equipment in the morning?

   _____

   _____

Clueless Crossword

Tuesday

education

This crossword is unlike any you've seen because it doesn't have any clues! Instead, fill in the grid according to the length of the word. We've filled in the first word for you.

3-letter words

all
arm
ate
doe
nag
one
pea

4-letter words

alas
area
cows
flew
kiwi

lion
meat
oval
talc
tank

5-letter words

after
anvil
drill
flows
lanai
leave
lever
nylon

ready
reefs
round
shank
stale
trace
trail
trees
woken

6-letter words

agreed
bundle
handle
Hawaii
laurel
trauma

7-letter words

college
connect
Indians
islands
ravioli
swallow

8-letter words

Colorado
engineer
summoned
tearooms

9-letter words

education
Wisconsin
ergonomic

ELEMENTARY, MY DEAR

Match the elements to their periodic symbols and hints.
If you need help, use an encyclopedia or the Internet.

1. gold

2. silver

3. copper

4. iron

5. mercury

6. platinum

7. tin

8. lead

a. Sn, asked the wizard for a heart

b. Pt, high record sales

c. Pb, Superman can't see through it

d. Au, caused miners quite a rush

e. Cu, plumbing fixtures

f. Hg, slippery liquid

g. Fe, important in the blood

h. Ag, the Lone Ranger's horse

PHOTO MATCH

Match the photo to the name of the musical instrument.

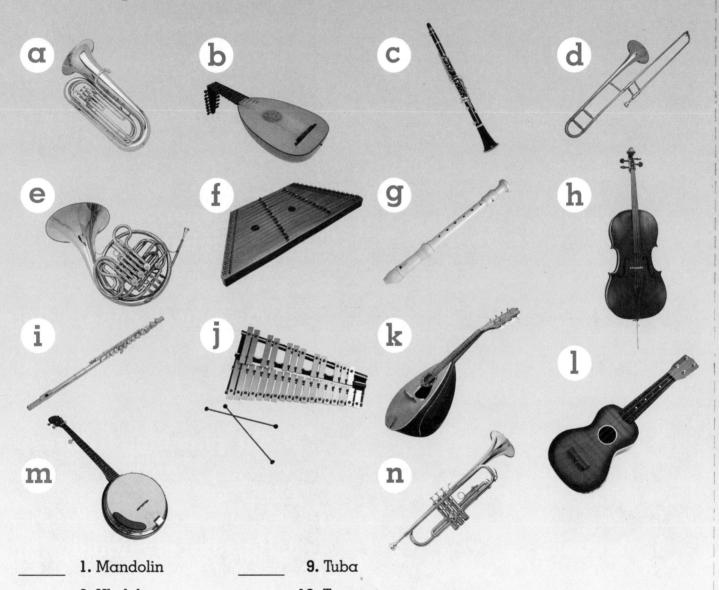

a b c d
e f g h
i j k l
m n

_____ 1. Mandolin   _____ 9. Tuba

_____ 2. Ukulele   _____ 10. Trumpet

_____ 3. Cello   _____ 11. French Horn

_____ 4. Banjo   _____ 12. Recorder

_____ 5. Lute   _____ 13. Dulcimer

_____ 6. Clarinet   _____ 14. Glockenspiel

_____ 7. Flute

_____ 8. Trombone

Mega Math

Can you solve the following problem? Assign different values for consonants and vowels. Can you detect a rule for solving the unknown amount?

Christi and her friend Jenna went to the mall for new clothes. They bought the following items:

- Jeans $22.00
- Shirts $18.00
- Wool Sweater   ?

How much did the wool sweater cost? What's the rule?

Riddles

1. The last four letters of me are one of a connected series. I am an action that protects while it cleanses. My last three letters can be found in the newspaper. What am I?

   _____

2. I am an insect but you might find another insect in my name. A very recognizable band was once named after me. What am I?

   _____

Word Pictures

Can you guess what these mean?

A
```
WW
AA
LL
KK
II
NN
GG
```

D

eating
run

F

DOWN

B

oysters

E
ONCE
TIME

G

HEART
HEART

C
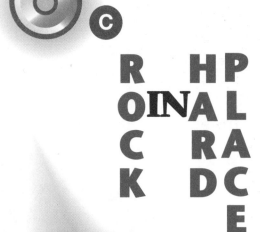
```
R   HP
OINAL
C   RA
K   D
```
RACE

H

TOWN

PROGRESSIVE WORDS

Can you get from the first word to the last by changing just one letter in each step?

Each word must be a real word!

VOWEL

_____

_____

_____

_____

LATER

FAMOUS PEOPLE FACTS

Match the Facts to the Famous Person!

If you need help, use an encyclopedia or the Internet.

1. George Armstrong Custer
2. Billie Jean King
3. Davy Crockett
4. Madonna Louise Ciccone

A. A tennis player born in Long Beach, California, she won titles (singles and doubles) in all four of the grand slam events of the women's tour, including 20 Wimbledon titles! In a battle of the sexes match in 1973 she defeated her male opponent, former U.S. Open and Wimbledon champ Bobby Riggs, in straight sets.

B. A character who became part of American folk legend, he was born in Tennessee and had careers in politics and the military. He was recognized for his hunting and scouting prowess. In 1836 he went to Texas and was killed in the infamous battle of the Alamo.

C. Born in Bay City, Michigan, in 1958, she is a singer, songwriter, and actress. She has sold millions of albums and is one of the most recognized entertainers in the world. Her movies include "Desperately Seeking Susan" (1985) and "Evita" (1996).

D. A military commander in both the Civil War and later on the American frontier, he gained fame more in defeat than in any of his victories. In 1876 at the battle of Little Bighorn, his force of over 200 men were greatly outnumbered and slaughtered.

Friday

Some people are very skilled when it comes to creating things such as chairs, sofas, electronics, etc. If you could create an object or something useful, what would it be? What kind of training would you need to do it?

_____

_____

_____

_____

_____

_____

_____

_____

_____

_____

_____

_____

_____

_____

_____

_____

_____

WORD PUZZLE

Word Box

P	A	R	T	S
A				E
R				N
T				D
S	E	N	D	S

Fill in the word square above using these nine letters:

- two each of the letters "O," "R" and "I"

- one each of the letters "D," "B" and "E"

This is a total of 25 letters (including the letters already given). The resulting words can be read both across and down.

Exploring Flight:
Testing Flight Variables

Adult supervision is recommended.

Changing an aircraft's shape and weight, as well as the places where weight is added or reduced, can make important differences in how the craft flies. ◆

Materials

paper clips

pencil or pen

scissors

Directions

Choose one of the jets you created on page 56, and conduct a series of tests to measure how certain variables affect its flight. The variables to test include:

• Adding paper clips to the nose and tail of the aircraft

• Adding tail flaps to the aircraft

Use the Jet Flier Data Sheet on the next page to record your estimates of how the variables will affect each flight as well as the actual results of each fight.

To create wing flaps for Trials 5 and 6, cut two .5 in. (1.3 cm) slits on the rear edge of each wing about 1 in. (2.5 cm) apart. Make the flaps by bending the cut sections up or down.

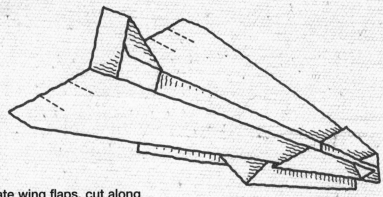

To create wing flaps, cut along the dotted lines. Bend the flaps up and down.

Jet Flier Data Sheet

Trial Number	Variable Added	Flight Pattern*	Approximate Speed**	Actual Flight Distance***
1	None			
2	Paper clip to nose			
3	Paper clip to tail			
4	Three paper clips to tail			
5	Wing flaps up			
6	Wing flaps down			

*Level, veer left/right, nose-dive, tailspin

**Fast, average, slow

***Average of three test flights

Odd Number Out

Can you figure out which fraction doesn't belong?

1 $\dfrac{18}{54}$ $\dfrac{13}{39}$ $\dfrac{26}{78}$ $\dfrac{4}{12}$ $\dfrac{6}{27}$

2 $\dfrac{4}{16}$ $\dfrac{12}{48}$ $\dfrac{28}{112}$ $\dfrac{24}{100}$ $\dfrac{20}{80}$

3 $\dfrac{6}{36}$ $\dfrac{48}{288}$ $\dfrac{12}{72}$ $\dfrac{18}{108}$ $\dfrac{30}{211}$

Cause and Effect

Record the cause and effect for each statement below:

1 Sam couldn't watch television for one week because he failed his science test.
Cause: Sam failed his science test.
Effect: Sam couldn't watch television for a week.

2 Ellen made a get-well card for her grandma who was very sick.
Cause:_____
Effect: _____

3 Rick's hair was hanging in his eyes, so he got a haircut.
Cause:_____
Effect: _____

4 Amber loved to draw so her mom got her art lessons for her birthday.
Cause:_____
Effect: _____

Optical Illusions

There are two women here. Can you find both the old woman and the young one?

Which way do you see the arrows pointing?

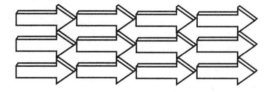

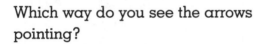

Are the blue lines straight or bent?

Which line is longer, x or s?

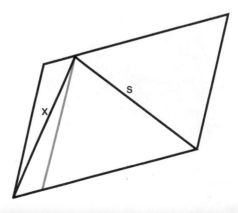

Hudson's Children

CHAPTER ELEVEN

The three travelers were unable to get tickets for the Polar Bear Express. This popular and luxurious train was fully booked by tourist groups. "I'm sorry," Trekk's dad said. "I've heard that this is one of last great rail trips in the world." He looked depressed.

"Maybe we can wait for the next one?" Trekk asked.

"Good plan," Terra said.

"You know, that gives me an idea," her uncle said. "Hang on." Terra's uncle returned, beaming. He had gotten seats on the Little Bear, the year-round regular train to Moosonee and James Bay. The Little Bear was not intended for tourists. It left later and took longer than the Polar Express, and it didn't make a round-trip on the same day, as the Polar Express did. Miraculously, Trekk's dad had also found lodging in Moosonee. They would leave on Friday and return on Saturday.

Trekk and Terra had ridden only metro trains in cities and were very excited. They got to watch the train connect passenger cars, freight cars, and flat cars. Their car didn't have the luxury of the Polar Bear Express, but it seemed more adventurous.

The train went north past the Abitibi River, once a highway of the fur trade. Then it slowed and stopped.

"Don't tell me the train got stuck," Trekk said.

"No, it's just picking up passengers," his dad said.

"I don't see any station here," Terra noted.

"The Little Bear is one of the last flag-stop trains in Canada. The train stops whenever someone flags it down. There are no roads up here, so it's the only way to go." Trekk and Terra craned their heads around to see a local family boarding.

The train made several such stops, and the 186 miles to Moosonee took nearly five hours. Along the way, they passed spruce forests, a giant hydroelectric dam, the great Moose River, and the prehistoric beaches of James Bay, or the inlet that drops down from Hudson Bay.

Moosonee was a bustling town. Still, the town maintained its sense of the past. The travelers took a "water taxi," or motorized canoe, to the town of Moose Factory, the oldest town in Ontario. There they saw Cree people living and working as they had for centuries, and they saw the restored buildings of the Hudson Bay Company, whose trading helped develop North America.

"Is this it, Dad?" Trekk asked. "Is this what you want to write about?"

"I don't have an idea yet," Trekk's dad admitted. "Can you think of something?" They spent the rest of the day taking in the frontier atmosphere.

As they boarded the train the next day, Trekk said, "Tell us more about Henry Hudson."

"It's not a happy ending, I'm afraid."

"Tell us anyway," Terra insisted.

Monday

Activity 11

Skill: Passage Comprehension

Match the item in the left column with a description from the right column.

_____ 1. Polar Bear Express

_____ 2. Abitibi

_____ 3. Little Bear

_____ 4. water taxi

_____ 5. Hudson Bay

_____ 6. flag stop

_____ 7. James Bay

_____ 8. Moose Factory

a. oldest town in Ontario

b. inlet that drops down from Hudson Bay

c. motorized canoe

d. bay named for an explorer

e. year-round transport to Moosonee and James Bay

f. river used by fur traders

g. luxurious nonstop train to Moosonee

h. unscheduled pickup of passengers

Math Maze
Circle With the Same Answer

- Using six different numbers inside of the circle, find the two separate equations that reach the total of "180."

- You can only use multiplication and division in your equations, either dividing your numbers then multiplying your total by another number or vice versa.

- Remember, you are only using three numbers from the circle per equation, for a total of six. And your two answers must both equal 180.

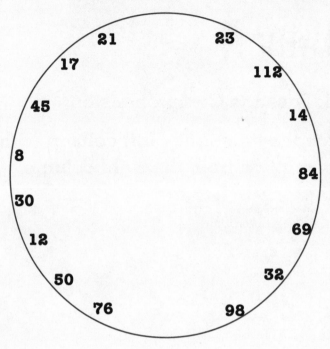

21 23 17 112 45 14 8 84 30 69 12 32 50 98 76

Antonyms, Synonyms or Homonyms

Antonyms mean the opposite. Synonyms mean the same. Homonyms sound alike but mean different. Identify the relationship for the words below.

1. reflect — think — _____

2. overcome — succumb — _____

3. course — coarse — _____

4. capital — capitol — _____

5. adviser — mentor — _____

6. casual — formal — _____

CATCH-22

Match the phrases to their meanings. If you need help, use an encyclopedia or the Internet.

1. push the envelope

2. cold turkey

3. by the skin of one's teeth

4. cut and dried

5. dressed to the nines

6. get one's goat

7. grain of salt

8. rock and a hard place

a. to annoy to the point of frustration

b. in a difficult position

c. dressed very elegantly

d. to view something with skepticism

e. to go beyond the known safe limits

f. a very narrow escape

g. to quit an addictive habit suddenly

h. routine, ordinary, obvious

ULTIMATE SCRAMBLE

Directions: Unscramble the letters below to form words.
Unscramble the circled letters from each word to solve the riddle.

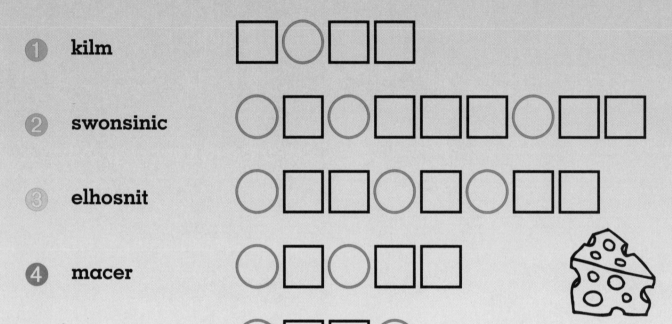

1 **kilm** ☐ ◯ ☐ ☐

2 **swonsinic** ◯ ☐ ◯ ☐ ☐ ☐ ◯ ☐ ☐

3 **elhosnit** ◯ ☐ ☐ ◯ ☐ ◯ ☐ ☐

4 **macer** ◯ ☐ ◯ ☐ ☐

5 **gesg** ◯ ☐ ☐ ◯

Hint: *It comes from "holy" cows.*

Answer:

◯ ◯ ◯ ◯ ◯

◯ ◯ ◯ ◯ ◯ ◯

Mega Math

Use $1 bills, $5 bills, $10 bills, $20 bills, and $50 bills to solve this problem.

Kana has four different kinds of bills. She has three times as many of her highest bill as she does her lowest bill. She has twice as many of her second highest bill as her highest bill. She has one more of her second lowest bill than her lowest bill. If she has $257 what are the bills? How many of each does she have?

Line Graph

Plot the sales data for the School Fundraiser on the graph and make a line graph by connecting the dots.

Sales

Week	Sales $
1	$447
2	$912
3	$769
4	$272
5	$589
6	$612
7	$788
8	$872
9	$941
10	$998

Sales axis: $1000, $950, $900, $850, $800, $750, $700, $650, $600, $550, $500, $450, $400, $350, $300, $250, $200, $150, $100

Weeks 1 2 3 4 5 6 7 8 9 10

Thursday

Angles

Right angles measure 90°

Acute angles measure less than 90°

Obtuse angles measure more than 90°

Identify each type of angle and circle the correct answer.

①

45°

Right   Acute   Obtuse

②

180°

Right   Acute   Obtuse

③

90°

Right   Acute   Obtuse

④

70°

Right   Acute   Obtuse

⑤

90°

Right   Acute   Obtuse

⑥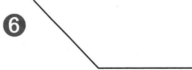

120°

Right   Acute   Obtuse

PROGRESSIVE WORDS

Can you get from the first word to the last by changing just one letter in each step?

Each word must be a real word!

JOKER

_____

_____

_____

_____

ROWED

FAMOUS PEOPLE FACTS

Match the Facts to the Famous Person!

If you need help, use an encyclopedia or the Internet.

1. Bruce Lee
2. Lady Diana Spencer
3. Wolfgang Amadeus Mozart
4. Aretha Franklin

A. She is known as the "Queen of Soul. "Born in Memphis, Tennessee, her family moved to Detroit where her father was a minister. Singing at her father's church she gained some notoriety and in 1966 signed with Atlantic Records. She is afraid of flying and often passes on invitations to perform if it requires air travel.

B. Martial arts actor. He was born in San Francisco but began his career in Hong Kong. One of his first American roles was on the television show The Green Hornet. He played the sidekick Kato. He gained international fame for such movies as "Enter the Dragon" (1973) and "Return of the Dragon" (1973). He died of brain edema at the age of 32.

C. A former kindergarten teacher, she married Prince Charles of Wales in a fairy-tale wedding in 1981. She bore two sons, William and Henry, before eventually splitting from Charles and divorcing in 1996. A champion of such causes as AIDS and the destruction of land mines, she remained popular with the people and was nicknamed the "Queen of Hearts." Tragically, she was killed in a car accident in Paris in 1997.

D. Born in Salzburg, Austria, he gained acclaim at a tender age for his compositions and mastery of the piano and violin. He has over 600 compositions to his credit including "The Marriage of Figaro" (1786), "Don Giovanni" (1787), and "The Magic Flute" (1791). He died at a young age in 1791.

Friday

Cameras and video cameras are all over the place these days. Describe the last picture or home video you were in, where you were, and why someone felt the need to capture that moment in history.

_____

_____

_____

_____

_____

_____

_____

_____

_____

_____

_____

_____

_____

_____

_____

WORD PUZZLE

Mystery Word

	A	B	C	D	E
1	J	O	R	L	S
2	A	N	Y	E	C
3	I	V	H	K	D
4	T	U	E	O	W
5	Q	L	F	M	G

- Use the box above to fill in the letters below.

- Each letter of the mystery word will use only one of the letters from each column below (top or bottom letter).

- Can you decipher the mystery word?

- Hint: He was a famous American!

C1	C4	B1	C5	C4	C1	E1	B5	D3
A1	D4	C5	E1	D2	B3	D2	A3	A4

Testing Direction with Orville and Wilbur

Adult supervision is recommended.

An experienced pilot can precisely control his or her aircraft's movement and direction. You can control an airplane in flight on three axes: roll, pitch and yaw. Roll occurs when the airplane wings are raised or lowered in opposite directions, causing the plane to rotate from side to side. Pitch results when the nose of the plane goes up and down, causing the entire plane to move up or down. Yaw occurs when the plane's nose aims left or right, causing the plane to turn left or right. ◆

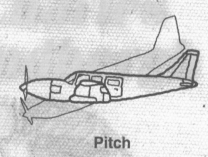

Pitch

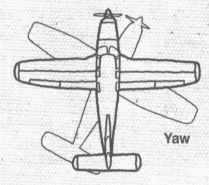

Yaw

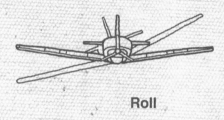

Roll

Materials

pen or pencil
paints, colored markers, or crayons

Directions

Subtle changes made to a paper airplane will impact how the plane flies. Use the non-flap plane you folded on pages 56-57, or fold a new jet. Next, print the name "Orville" clearly on the top of one wing and "Wilbur" on top of the other. See how modifications you make to the jet's wings change its flight path by putting it through a series of test flights.
Use the same amount of throw (thrust) for each test. Record your results in the "Charting Directions" form on the next page.

When you have finished with the test, decorate your new jet using markers, paints or crayons.

Saturday

Charting Directions

Note: For "up" and "down" wing positions, bend the wing up or down at a 45-degree angle from its level (horizontal) position.

45°

Test Flight Number	Wing Position	Flight Direction (level veers left, veers right nosedives, tailspins)	Flight Distance
1	Orville and Wilbur level		
2	Orville up, Wilbur level		
3	Orville and Wilbur up		
4	Wilbur up, Orville level		
5	Orville and Wilbur down		
6	Orville down, Wilbur level		
7	Wilbur down, Orville level		

Which force or forces are acting on the jet to explain the results of your test?

_____

_____

More Mega Math

Each of the symbols represents a number between 1 - 10. Can you figure out which number should fill in the blank?

Brain Teaser

Can you identify these objects?

a   b   c

_____   _____   _____

d   e   f

_____   _____   _____

Word Problems

Use addition, subtraction, multiplication or division to solve the word problems below.

1 Company X sold 700,000 T-shirts this year. Last year they sold 80% of what they sold this year. What did they sell last year?

2 XYZ Elementary School has 24 teachers and a total of 528 students. What is the average number of students in each class?

3 Happytime Amusement Park has a total of 17 rides. The average wait in line for each is 30 minutes. How many rides could you go in one 8 hour day if you took one hour for lunch?

4 Barry drinks two gallons of milk each week. How many gallons of milk does he drink in a year?

5 You want to buy a stereo that costs $169.00. You have $76.00 in your bank account and your aunt said she is sending you $40.00 for your birthday. How much money do you still need to buy that stereo?

6 Your baseball team has a record so far of 10 wins to 6 losses. There is a total of 20 games in the season. What is the best possible record your team could finish with this season? What is the worst possible record your team could finish with?

Hudson's Children

CHAPTER TWELVE

As Little Bear moved southward, Trekk's dad told of Henry Hudson's attempts to find a Northeast Passage to China.

"Hudson's idea was to sail to the Pole, turn east, and then work his way down the other side of the world. Ice blocked him twice and winds blew him south, so he found New York Harbor and the Hudson River on the third voyage."

"Pretty far off course," Trekk said.

"That's right. He had heard from Captain John Smith and others that there might be a Northwest Passage across what is now the United States. On his last voyage he discovered Hudson Bay, but ice trapped him in James Bay. Food ran out. Mutiny erupted. Hudson, his young son, and some loyal crewmen were set adrift in a small boat."

"The rest of the crew just left them?" Terra asked.

"No one ever saw or heard from them again, but legend claims that he survived. Marks looking like 'HH' were found. One Inuit story tells of finding a boat with dead men and a live boy. Nobody really knows."

"How sad," Trekk said.

Back in Cochrane, the group began the trip home. They restocked and headed for Sault Ste. Marie.

They took one last afternoon to fish near Chapleau. They watched a loon and tried quietly to approach it with the canoe. Every time they got near, it dove and disappeared. Suddenly, Terra had a terrific strike on her line. She yanked the pole and began to reel when she saw the loon had taken her reel. To her horror, the loon dove under the canoe."If we don't get him, he'll drown," her uncle said. After some awful moments, a thrashing loon surfaced. Trekk jumped in and put his jacket over the bird. They brought it to shore. Luckily, the hooks had done little damage. Gently, Trekk's dad cut the bird loose and put it in the water. The loon swam weakly away.

"Do you think he'll make it?" Terra asked.

"He has a chance," her uncle replied.

"More than Henry Hudson's young son had," Trekk said, unable to shake the story from his mind.

Terra said, "That's it!"

"What?" Trekk said.

"What if he did make it? What if he survived?"

"Think of all he would have had to go through and learn," Trekk said.

"You two have just solved my problem!" Trekk's dad said. "There's my story!"

"'Hudson's Child,'" said Terra.

"'A Legend of Hope,'" Trekk added.

"That's pretty good. This could turn into a whole book. Can I count on you two for ideas?"

"You bet," the cousins said, laughing.

On fire with ideas, Trekk and Terra promised to work together by e-mail and telephone. Their Ontario trip was ending, but a new adventure was just beginning.

Monday

Activity 12

Skill: Summarizing

Put these events and places Terra and Trekk experienced in the right order, beginning with the earliest one. Number the events from 1 to 10.

_____ Hornepayne, after being stuck in the sand

_____ Chapleau and the loon

_____ Entering Canada at Sault Ste. Marie

_____ René Brunelle Provincial Park and the bears

_____ Cochrane and the train station

_____ Lake Superior Provincial Park and the fearsome squirrel

_____ Moosonee and James Bay

_____ Kapuskasing and the moose

_____ Wawa and the giant goose

_____ Back from James Bay aboard Little Bear

	Rodney	Byron	Robert	Isabella	Iris	Violin	Guitar	Drums	Trombone	Saxophone	Mr. Leeves	Mrs. Kim	Ms. Hasad	Mr. Owen	Miss Kraus
Gist															
Rothschild															
Sylvester															
Templeton															
Lane															
Mr. Leeves															
Mrs. Kim															
Ms. Hasad															
Mr. Owen															
Miss Kraus															
Violin															
Guitar															
Drums															
Trombone															
Saxophone															

Iris and her four friends take music lessons. They each have different teachers and play different instruments. Based on the clues below, can you determine each child's first and last name, their teacher's name, and the instrument they play?

1. Two of the three boys play string instruments.

2. Isabella's last name begins with the same letter as her instructor's.

3. Byron, the Sylvester child, and the child that plays the trombone all have female instructors.

4. Iris, the boy who plays the drums (Mr. Owen is his instructor), the child who takes lessons from Miss Kraus, and the violin player all live in the same neighborhood.

5. Rodney really likes his instructor, Miss Kim, whereas the Rothschild boy, the Gist child, and Robert think that their instructors are a little strict.

FAMOUS INVENTORS

Match the famous inventors & their inventions.
If you need help, use an encyclopedia or the Internet.

1. An African-American inventor who invented 300 uses for peanuts and developed a revolutionary crop-rotation method.

a. Thomas Alva Edison (1847-1931)

2. Corn flakes

b. Alexander Graham Bell (1847-1922)

3. Bifocals

c. George Washington Carver (1860-1943)

4. The telephone

d. Alfred Nobel (1833-1896)

5. A way to treat milk, for longer storage without it developing microbes (pasteurization).

e. Will Keith Kellogg (1860-1951)

6. Established a prize fund. The prize is awarded annually for achievements in Physics, Chemistry, Physiology or Medicine, Literature and Peace.

f. King C. Gillette (1855-1932)

7. The light bulb

g. Benjamin Franklin (1706-1790)

8. The disposable "safety" razor blade

h. Louis Pasteur (1822-1895)

ODD NUMBER OUT

Can you figure out which number doesn't belong?

1. 112   54   84   49   287

2. 88   168   73   96   120

3. 18   104   198   27   117

WORD GAMES

Can you guess the relationship?

1. George   Richard   Henry   Edward

2. octopus   worm   jellyfish   beetle

3. lion   shark   wolf   owl

Mega Math

Can you solve the following problem? Assign different values for consonants and vowels. Can you detect a rule for solving the unknown amount?

Jessica and Kara went to the toy store and purchased these great toys:

- Hoola Hoop $10.75
- Jigsaw Puzzle $11.00
- Comic Books   ?

How much did the comic books cost?

What's the rule?

Optical Illusions

Do these rows appear to be slanted? They're parallel!

Thursday

Word Pictures

Can you guess what these mean?

A DANCE DANCE / DANCE DANCE DANCE / DANCE DANCE

B cat cat dog dogs

C 134SAFETY624

D Pudproofding

E MOMANON

F Books TAPE

G 4 3 2 1 (arrow)

H Milk Milk Milk

I APPLE (upside down)

J mailmailmailmailmail
mailmailmailmailmail
mailmailmailmailmail
mailmailmailmailmail
mailmailmailmailmail
mailmailmailmailmail
mailmailmailmailmail

K S H O W E R S

L tibackme

M working / time

N LITTLELITTLE / LATELATE

O KIND KIND (second reversed)

P POTATOES

164

PROGRESSIVE WORDS

Can you get from the first word to the last by changing just one letter in each step?

Each word must be a real word!

PANTS

_____

_____

_____

RUSTY

FAMOUS PEOPLE FACTS

Match the Facts to the Famous Person!

If you need help, use an encyclopedia or the Internet.

1. Jackie Robinson
2. Helen Keller
3. Albert Einstein
4. Elizabeth Taylor

A. Born in Ulm, Germany, he was an unimpressive student. In fact, his parents wondered if he was retarded. He would go on to earn a Ph.D. in Physics and created the famous equation $E=mc^2$ which described the relationship between matter and energy. He later emigrated to the United States to avoid the Nazis during WWII and became a spokesperson for peace. He died in 1955.

B. He made history as the first African-American to play major league baseball. He played for the Brooklyn Dodgers beginning in 1947. His career was filled with hardships as players and fans targeted him with racial slurs and threats. In spite of this, he went on to win a batting title and was named league MVP. His Dodgers won their first World Series in 1955. In 1962 he was inducted into the Hall of Fame.

C. A Hollywood legend, she was born in London, England. Her career began early with roles in "There's One Born Every Minute" (1942) and "National Velvet" (1944). She has been married an incredible eight times! She is also known for having violet-colored eyes.

D. She became blind and deaf as an infant. Her teacher, Anne Sullivan (who also became famous and was nicknamed the "Miracle Worker"), taught her to read braille and finger-spell. She graduated from Radcliffe College in 1904 and went on to become a lecturer and author on behalf of the blind.

Friday

You're the president of a new company that manufactures tennis shoes. It's your job to write a commercial that will be very successful and sell a bunch of shoes. What will your commercial say?

_____

_____

_____

_____

_____

_____

_____

_____

_____

_____

_____

_____

_____

_____

_____

_____

_____

Twisted Word Search

H	G	N	J	F	F	Z	O	K
B	T	H	S	P	A	E	D	V
N	Y	E	A	I	X	L	W	L
C	B	N	D	M	R	U	G	Z
N	A	Q	U	E	E	B	C	E
S	W	O	O	D	T	R	R	J
M	H	T	A	Y	I	I	B	Q
A	C	V	X	C	A	U	P	K
D	A	I	A	N	T	R	F	G
A	N	C	H	S	Z	L	F	I
Y	Q	S	O	M	T	X	J	E
V	W	E	P	R	D	G	R	I
E	F	B	A	A	H	E	P	O
C	R	D	I	W	Q	C	K	L
N	A	N	J	E	D	U	H	B
U	C	O	Z	G	V	E	P	I
W	E	U	A	H	Y	G	N	E
P	B	K	R	N	C	A	R	M
Z	F	A	O	M	I	O	A	U
T	T	N	C	E	F	R	D	W
R	C	H	I	X	K	S	N	M

In this word search the letter formations are "wrapped" around the boxes in four different ways. Check the examples below. Watch out. Words may be intertwined!

Words

America	Ghana
Algeria	China
Denmark	Spain
Mexico	Fiji
France	Cuba
Canada	Peru

7-Letter Word

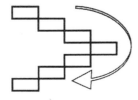

6-Letter Word

5-Letter Word

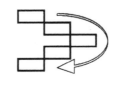

4-Letter Word

Exploring Flight:
Modern Jetliner
Adult supervision is recommended.

Wilbur and Orville would be amazed. Modern airplanes weigh many tons, carry huge quantities of cargo, and travel vast distances at unbelievable speeds. For example, the modern 757 aircraft is a flying laboratory for the National Aeronautics and Space Administration (NASA) and is equipped with digital cockpit controls and displays. In addition, this commercial 757 jetliner has flown the equivalent of nearly 25,000 round-trips between the earth and the moon and weighs a hefty 255,000 lbs. (115,666 kg)! ◆

Materials
scissors
tape
paper clip
colored markers, paints, or
  crayons

Directions
Create your own modern jetliner by following these steps.

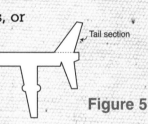
Tail section

Figure 5

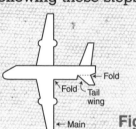
Fold
Fold
Tail wing
Main wing

Figure 6

Figure 2

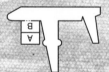

1. Cut out the template on the next page. *See Figure 1.*
2. Cut along the dashed lines.
3. Fold the plane body in half. *See Figure 2.*
4. Fold A inward to B. Fold B into the plane's body. *See Figure 3.*

Figure 3

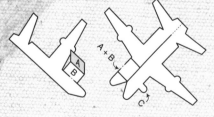

5. Insert tab C into the slot at the bottom of B. *See Figure 4.*

Figure 4

6. Fold the tail section in half, and slide it all the way into the slot in the back of the plane. Tape the tail securely to the plane body. *See Figure 5.*

7. Bend the main wings and the tail wings up to a normal flying position. *See Figure 6.*

8. Tape the nose of the airplane.

9. Add a paper clip to the nose of the airplane. *See Figure 7.*

10. Research in the library to see how modern jetliners are painted today. Decorate your plane so that it looks like an authentic modern jetliner. Then have fun and let it fly!

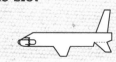

Figure 7

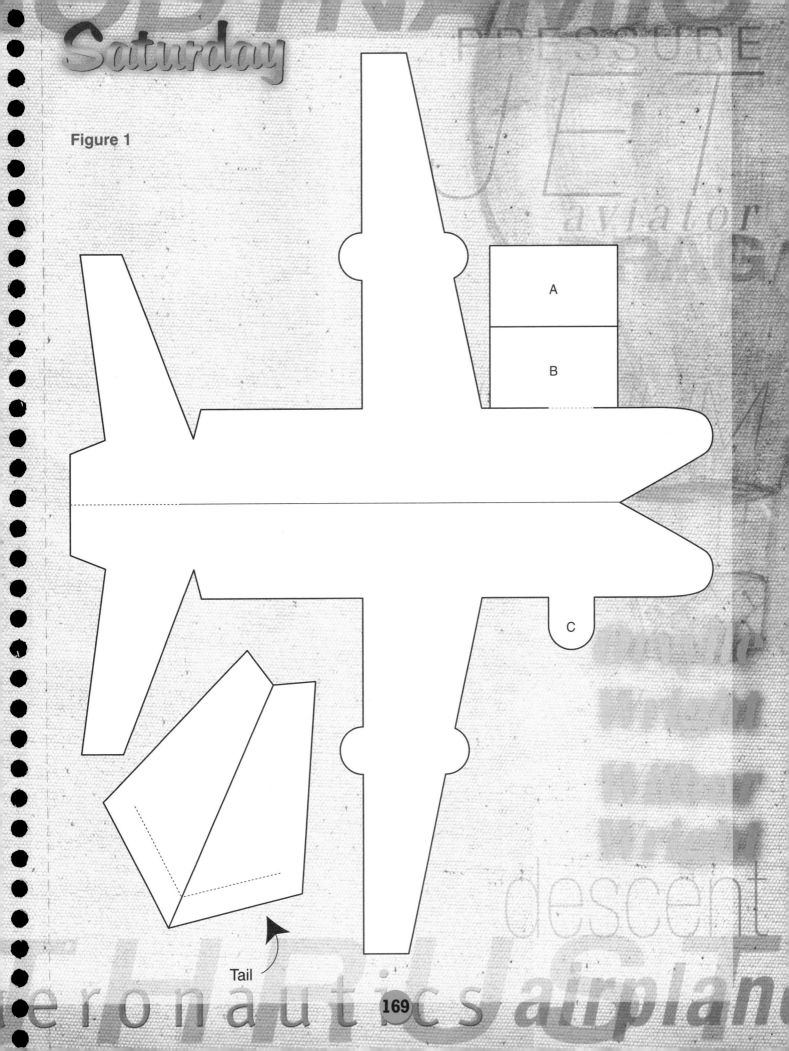

Figure 1

A

B

C

Tail

Adjectives and Predicate Adjectives

Adjectives **precede the nouns they describe.**

Predicate **adjectives follow a verb and describe the subject of the sentence.**

A. Adjective   B. Predicate Adjective

Determine whether each sentence contains an adjective or predicate adjective and label accordingly with A or B.

1 We watched the sad movie.   _____

2 The concert was loud.   _____

3 I dreamed of a wise owl.   _____

4 The snow felt cold.   _____

5 The cookies smell so good.   _____

6 The losing team needs a coach.   _____

Point of View

Stories are written from different points of view.
In First person narratives the writer is in the story and uses I, me, my, etc., in their descriptions.

In Third person narratives the writer is not part of the story.

For each sentence determine which point of view is used and circle first or third.

1. The truck driver struggles to stay awake at the wheel.   First   Third

2. I kept climbing until my legs wouldn't carry me any further.   First   Third

3. It was inevitable that my mother would figure out that I lied.   First   Third

4. The sailor grew sad as his shore leave came to an end.   First   Third

5. Every astronaut went through intensive physical training.   First   Third

6. My coach keeps pushing us to work harder.   First   Third

7. The chef lost his temper when the restaurant patron complained and sent their food back.   First   Third

8. Whenever my family goes on vacation, we have a good time.   First   Third

Answers

MONDAY Page 5

Trekk's home is in New York.
Cousin Terra is from New Mexico.
Trekk's dad is a writer.
Terra's mother is an archaeologist.

TUESDAY Page 6

Math Maze

Word Games

1. Nylon. The rest are natural fibers.
2. Dendrite. The rest are teeth.
3. Robin. The others hibernate.

TUESDAY Matching Page 7

1. f	2. e	3. a	4. g
5. d	6. c	7. h	8. b

WEDNESDAY Page 9
Mega Math

Tom has the following coins:

6 silver dollars	$ 6.00		11 half dollars	$ 5.50
6 half dollars	$ 3.00	OR	11 quarters	$ 2.75
6 dimes	$ 0.60		11 dimes	$ 1.10
6 nickels	$ 0.30		11 nickels	$ 0.55
TOTAL	$ 9.90		TOTAL	$ 9.90

Place Value

1. 60,000,000 + 5,000,000 + 400,000 + 40,000 + 4,000 + 200 + 90 + 9
2. 1,000,000 + 900,000 + 60,000 + 7,000 + 800 + 20 + 2
3. 400,000,000,000 + 70,000,000,000 + 9,000,000,000 + 500,000,000 + 80,000,000 + 6,000,000 + 200,000 + 80,000 + 6,000 + 500 + 30 + 3
4. 800,000,000 + 30,000,000 + 1,000,000 + 400,000 + 80,000 + 1,000 + 900 + 10 + 5

WEDNESDAY Ultimate Scramble Page 8

1. Calendar
2. Lunch
3. Apple
4. Attendance
5. Recess

Answer:
Teacher's Pet

THURSDAY Page 11
Progressive Words

RIDER
RISER
RISES
ROSES
HOSES
HOPES

This is a suggested answer. There may be more than one correct answer.

Famous People Facts

1. c   2. a   3. d   4. b

THURSDAY Page 10
Balance the Checking Account

Date	Deposit	Withdrawal	Balance
Jan. 2nd	$208.00		$675.00
Jan. 9th		$88.11	$586.89
Jan. 16th		$256.62	$330.27
Jan. 23rd	$1,211.47		$1,541.74
Jan. 30th		$118.98	$1,422.76
Feb. 6th	$526.50		$1,949.26
Feb. 13th		$733.69	$1,215.57
Feb. 20th	$64.99		$1,280.56
Feb. 27th		$412.53	$868.03
March 6th	$75.75		$943.78
March 13th		$67.88	$875.90
March 20th	$298.98		$1,174.88

FRIDAY Word Puzzle Page 13

C3	B2 L	A3 A	B1	B4 I	E1 N	B3	D3 T
D4 C	A3	C1	E5 R	C5	A1	A5 E	C4

SATURDAY Page 15

The Science of Flight
3. The paper rises.

SUNDAY   Page 16
More Mega Math

 = 6   ▲ = 4   ● = 2

Answer: ? = 8

Fractions, Decimals & Percentages

1. $\frac{1}{100}$ = 0.01 = 1%   5. $\frac{98}{100}$ = 0.98 = 98%

2. $\frac{13}{100}$ = 0.13 = 13%   6. $\frac{33}{100}$ = 0.33 = 33%

3. $\frac{66}{100}$ = 0.66 = 66%   7. $\frac{32}{100}$ = 0.32 = 32%

4. $\frac{77}{100}$ = 0.77 = 77%   8. $\frac{42}{100}$ = 0.42 = 42%

SUNDAY   Page 17
Similes, Metaphors and Personification

1. a   5. b
2. a   6. a
3. b   7. c
4. c   8. b

WEEK 2 • Pages 18–31

MONDAY   Page 19

Answers will vary. Possible responses:

1. Trekk looked taller, and he had changed his hair.
2. Terra is used to flying alone now.
3. They met in Michigan to pick up camping equipment from a friend.
4. They traveled northwest.
5. They saw cherry and apple orchards as they drove through Michigan.
6. They pitch tents and build a campfire. Terra and Trekk take a moonlight hike.
7. The group plans to go sailing the next day.

TUESDAY   Page 21
Matching

1. e   5. g
2. c   6. d
3. f   7. a
4. h   8. b

WEDNESDAY   Page 22
Photo Match

1. m   6. c   11. e
2. k   7. f   12. j
3. l   8. d   13. n
4. a   9. g   14. i
5. b   10. h

WEDNESDAY   Page 23
Mega Math
Potato chips cost $4.70.
Consonants are $0.10 each and vowels are $1.00 each.

Punctuation & Capitalization Quiz
Sara couldn't wait for summer vacation to begin! Her family was planning a trip to Europe. "Mom, when are we leaving for our trip?" asked Sara.

"We will leave on June 30," answered Sara's mother.

TUESDAY   Page 20
Odd Number Out

1st line: 63, all others are products of 12.
(2x12=24, 6x12=72, 9x12=108, 1x12=12)

2nd line: 71, all others are products of 11.
(3x11=33, 12x11=132, 6x11=66, 1x11=11)

3rd line: 92, all others are products of 14.
(4x14=56, 1x14=14, 2x14=28, 7x14=98)

Adverbial Phrases

1. She ate her hamburger (in a hurry.)
2. He lost his watch (in the back yard.)
3. You better run as (fast as you can.)
4. My uncle works nights and sleeps (during the day.)
5. My brother ran on the treadmill (for an hour.)
6. The mechanic tuned the car (with precision.)

THURSDAY Page 24
Finding Radius, Diameter and Circumference

	Circumference	Diameter	Radius
1.	6 ft	2 ft	1 ft
2.	42 cm	14 cm	7 cm
3.	36 m	12 m	6 m
4.	24 mm	8 mm	4 mm
5.	4,872 cm	1,624 cm	812 cm
6.	75 mi	25 mi	12.5 mi
7.	933 in	311 in	155.5 in
8.	307.2 yd	102.4 yd	51.2 yd
9.	2.64 km	0.88 km	0.44 km
10.	1,263 ft	421 ft	210.5 ft
11.	22,836 cm	7,612 cm	3,806 cm
12.	0.69 mm	0.23 mm	0.115 mm
13.	573 m	191 m	95.5 m
14.	2.997 cm	0.999 cm	0.4995 cm

THURSDAY Page 25
Progressive Words

TWINE
SWINE
SPINE
SPITE
SPITS
SPOTS

This is a suggested answer.
There may be more than one
correct answer.

Famous People Facts

1. b   2. d   3. a   4. c

FRIDAY Page 27
Word Puzzle

D	R	A	F	T
R	E	F	E	R
A	F	I	R	E
F	E	R	N	S
T	R	E	S	S

SATURDAY Page 28 – 29
Flying Is a Weighty Matter

Falling to Earth
3. Answers will vary but may include: The ball of paper falls faster than the flat paper. The flat paper has more lift generated by its shape. The crumpled paper is pulled to the ground by gravity.

Holding Up Objects With Water and Air
5. The penny sinks because it is heavier than an equal amount of water underneath it.

Let's Take a Balloon Ride!
2. An average-sized helium balloon takes 5 paper clips.
5 ¥ .01 = .05 ounces

SUNDAY Grid Logic Page 30

	Nathan	Tino	Vanessa	Azra	Maple	Oak	Birch	Spruce
Kamali	X	X	X	O	X	O	X	X
Rodriguez	X	X	O	X	X	X	X	O
Bahaligia	X	O	X	X	X	X	O	X
Feinstein	O	X	X	X	O	X	X	X
Maple	O	X	X	X				
Oak	X	X	X	O				
Birch	X	O	X	X				
Spruce	X	X	O	X				

Answer:
1. Nathan Feinstein/Maple
2. Tino Bahaligia/**Birch**
3. Vanessa Rodriguez/Spruce
4. Azra Kamali/Oak

SUNDAY Page 31
Prefixes

1. disappear
2. misunderstand
3. preview
   or review
4. reread or misread
5. unsure
6. nonstop

MONDAY Crossword Page 33

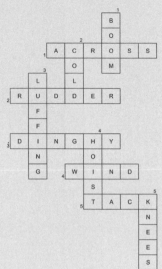

TUESDAY Page 34 Math Maze

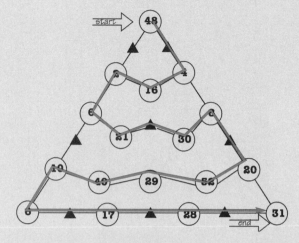

Word Games

1. Carp. The others are saltwater fish.
2. Pig. The others provide milk that can be consumed by humans.
3. Banana. The rest are fruits with pits.

WEDNESDAY Ultimate Scramble Page 36

1. bananas
2. primate
3. evolve
4. jungle
5. chunky

Answer:
Monkey's Uncle

Mega Math Page 37

Jennifer has the following coins:

10 silver dollars	$10.00
10 half dollars	$ 5.00
10 quarters	$ 2.50
10 dimes	$ 1.00
10 nickels	$ 0.50
TOTAL	$19.00

Multiplication of Fractions

1. e
2. a
3. f
4. d
5. c
6. b

TUESDAY Matching Page 35

1. d	2. f	3. a	4. b
5. c	6. g	7. h	8. e

THURSDAY Page 39
Progressive Words

MALLS
MILLS
MILES
PILES
PIPES
PIPER

This is a suggested answer.
There may be more than one correct answer.

Famous People Facts

1. d   2. a   3. b   4. c

THURSDAY Page 38
Pie Graphs

City Name	Percent	Decimal	Population
City A	32%	0.32	160,160
City B	28%	0.28	140,140
City C	22%	0.22	110,110
City D	11%	0.11	55,055
City E	3%	0.03	15,015
City F	4%	0.04	20,020

FRIDAY Word Puzzle Page 41

E5	E4	A4	A2 C	B3	C2 I	E5	B4 I
C4 Z	A5 U	B3 C	B3	E2 H	D1	D4 N	A1

SATURDAY Page 43

Spinning Maple Seeds

Because of the many variables involved (e.g., thickness of the paper, angle of the flap, curl of the paper, wind direction/strength), there are really no right or wrong answers here. Students are learning how to systematically conduct tests by following directions and to observe, interpret and communicate their test results.

SUNDAY

Calculating Discount Percentages   Page 45

1. d	4. b
2. a	5. f
3. e	6. c

WEEK 4 • Pages 46–59

MONDAY Page 47

Answers: 1. b; 2. c; 3. d; 4. a; 5. d; 6. c

TUESDAY Page 48

Odd Number Out

1st row: 20. All others are perfect squares.
(6x6=36, 4x4=16, 3x3=9, 8x8=64)

2nd Row: 42. (5x5=25, 2x2=4, 7x7=49, 6x6=36)

3rd Row: 56. (1x1=1, 4x4=16, 8x8=64, 9x9=81)

Comparative and Superlative

1. large	larger	largest
2. high	higher	highest
3. big	bigger	biggest
4. quick	quicker	quickest
5. long	longer	longest
6. fast	faster	fastest

TUESDAY Page 49
Matching

1. c	5. f
2. d	6. h
3. e	7. b
4. g	8. a

SUNDAY   Page 44

More Mega Math

■ = 2   ▲ = 3   ● = 1

Answer: ? = 5

Suffixes

1. agreement	4. happiness
2. hopeless	5. kindly
3. believable	6. appearance

WEDNESDAY Page 50
Clueless Crossword

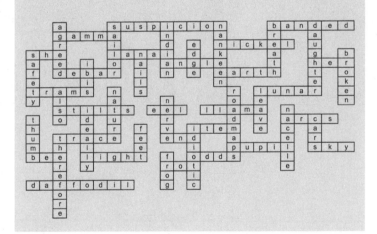

WEDNESDAY   Page 51
Mega Math

Favors cost $3.50.
Consonants are $0.50 each and vowels are $0.75 each.

Ratio Quiz

1. c	3. a	5. b
2. f	4. e	6. d

THURSDAY   Finding Area   Page 52

1. Area = 150 cm

2. Area = 75 in

3. Area = 102 m

4. Area = 344.52 mm

5. Area = 2236.5 ft

6. Area = 24.2 km

THURSDAY   Page 53
Progressive Words

BLINK
SLINK
SLICK
STICK
STUCK

This is a suggested answer. There may be more than one correct answer.

Famous People Facts

1. b   2. c   3. d   4. a

FRIDAY   Word Puzzle   Page 55

		D	R		W				
		E	E			H	J	R	
						A	A	A	
						L	G	U	
T	E				E				
O	S								
R	I					I	A		
T	O		M	Y		G	N		
		S	O	E		U	A		
			N	K					
F	O			A		P	T		
L	G		K			A	O		
A	N	E	T		B	R	R		
M	I	L	N		O	A			
		E	A				D	K	
G		P	H			U	C		
C	O					L			
	O	O					L		
	S	B		S	L			A	
E	R			E	A		M		
A					A				

SATURDAY   Page 57

The Great Glorious Glider Airplane Race

9. If you are right-handed, this is your stronger arm, so it would provide more thrust power, and vice versa.

SUNDAY   Page 58
More Mega Math

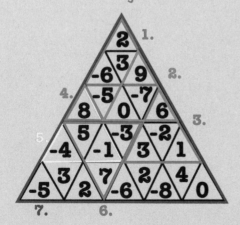

1. 2 + 3 − 6 + 9 = 8
2. 9 − 7 + 0 + 6 = 8
3. 6 − 2 + 3 + 1 = 8
4. 8 = 8
5. 8 + 5 − 4 − 1 = 8
6. 5 − 3 − 1 + 7 = 8
7. The entire triangle adds up to 8.

Brain Teaser   Page 58

Answer: Shoe, all the others are types of cakes.

SUNDAY   Homonyms   Page 59

1. I have an eyelash in my eye.
2. My mother needs to go by the bakery to buy a cake.
3. Did you know that there are no more tickets available?
4. My father's sister, Aunt Sara, has an ant farm.
5. Where did you find the Halloween costume you plan to wear?
6. Sam's dad said, "Son, put on some sunblock. That sun is really strong."
7. Did you hear the teacher tell us to come over here?
8. I read the book with the red cover.

WEEK 5 • Pages 60–73

MONDAY   Page 61

1. Detroit
2. White Cloud
3. Petoskey
4. Mackinaw City
5. Whitefish Point
6. Sault Ste Marie
7. Lake Superior Provincial Park

TUESDAY   Page 62
Math Maze

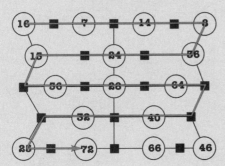

Word Games

1. They are all things that float.
2. They are all things that sting.
3. They are all first names of U.S. presidents. (John F. Kennedy, Abraham Lincoln, George Washington, Ronald Reagan)

Matching   Page 63

1. c
2. h
3. g
4. f
5. d
6. a
7. b
8. e

WEDNESDAY
Ultimate Scramble   Page 64

1. Planet
2. Comet
3. Asteroid
4. Atmosphere
5. Celestial

Answer:
Space Cadet

WEDNESDAY   Page 65
Mega Math

Holly has the following coins:

42 silver dollars	$42.00
42 quarters	$10.50
42 nickels	$ 2.10
42 pennies	$ 0.42
TOTAL	$55.02

Comparative and Superlative

Word	Comparative	Superlative
1. horrible	more horrible	most horrible
2. generous	more generous	most generous
3. terrific	more terrific	most terrific
4. delicious	more delicious	most delicious
5. ridiculous	more ridiculous	most ridiculous
6. complicated	more complicated	most complicated

THURSDAY   Plot the Coordinates   Page 66

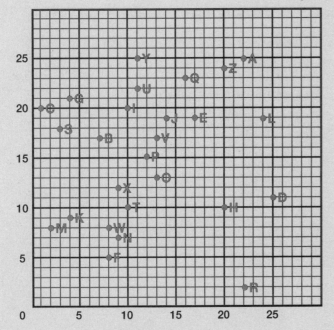

THURSDAY   Page 67
Progressive Words

GLASS
CLASS
CRASS
CROSS
CROWS
CROWN

This is a suggested answer. There may be more than one correct answer.

Famous People Facts

1. c   2. d   3. a   4. b

FRIDAY   Word Puzzle   Page 69

D5 A	E1	C5	E2 B	D3	E1 A	D1 N
C4	B5 R	E1	B4 A	C2 I	A3	C1

WEEK 5 • Continued

SATURDAY   Page 71

Drag Racing to the Ground

Test Results chart: The paper clips and clothespins should hit at approximately the same time regardless of height; the stacked liners will hit before the single liner.

Students should conclude that the shape of an object affects its drag, and in this case, the object's weight makes no difference. The flat bottom of the muffin liner creates drag that slows down its progress—in this case, its descent.

SUNDAY   Fantasy vs. Reality   Page 73

1. Fantasy
2. Reality
3. Fantasy
4. Fantasy
5. Reality
6. Fantasy
7. Reality
8. Fantasy

SUNDAY   Page 72
More Mega Math

 = 9   ▲ = 4   ● = 7

Answer: ? = 13

Converting Fractions to Decimals

1. $\dfrac{17}{1000} = 0.017$

2. $5\dfrac{199}{1000} = 5.199$

3. $6\dfrac{35}{10000} = 6.0035$

4. $\dfrac{999}{10000} = 0.0999$

5. $5\dfrac{5}{1000} = 5.005$

6. $792\dfrac{1777}{10000} = 792.1777$

7. $\dfrac{84}{1000} = 0.084$

8. $2\dfrac{27}{10000} = 2.0027$

WEEK 6 • Pages 74–87

MONDAY   Page 75

Answers will vary. Possible responses:

1. All the other people were used to the cool temperatures, but Trekk and Terra weren't.

2. The Ojibway are a native people who settled the area long before the French.

3. The Ojibway word Wawa means "Wild Goose" or "Land of Big Goose."

4. The people of the town wanted to attract visitors.

5. They noticed fewer and fewer signs of people.

6. The clearings were built to park construction equipment when the highway was being built.

7. The truck got stuck in the soft sand.

8. The travelers will be behind in their travels. The travelers could experience unexpected adventure.

TUESDAY   Page 76

Odd Number Out
1. 35   2. 18   3. 88
All the others are prime numbers.
(Their only factors are 1 and themselves.)

Comparative and Superlative Exceptions

1. good   better   best
2. less   lesser   least
3. some   more   most
4. bad   worse   worst

TUESDAY
Matching   Page 77

1. e
2. g
3. h
4. b
5. a
6. d
7. f
8. c

WEDNESDAY Page 78
Grid Logic

	Claire	Raj	Indira	Sophia	Justin	Nashville, TN	San Francisco, CA	Seattle, WA	Atlanta, GA	Honolulu, HI	April 10th	June 18th	July 12th	July 30th	August 5th
Nandi	X	X	O	X	X	O	X	X	X	X	O	X	X	X	X
Bass	X	X	X	X	O	X	X	X	X	O	X	O	X	X	X
Patel	X	O	X	X	X	X	X	O	X	X	X	X	X	X	O
Danner	O	X	X	X	X	X	O	X	X	X	X	X	O	X	X
Truscello	X	X	X	O	X	X	X	O	X	X	X	X	X	O	X
April 10th	X	X	O	X	X	O	X	X	X	X
June 18th	X	X	X	X	O	X	X	X	X	O
July 12th	O	X	X	X	X	X	O	X	X	X
July 30th	X	X	X	O	X	X	X	O	X	X
August 5th	X	O	X	X	X	X	X	O	X	X
Nashville, TN	X	X	O	X	X
San Francisco, CA	O	X	X	X	X
Seattle, WA	X	X	X	O	X
Atlanta, GA	X	O	X	X	X
Honolulu, HI	X	X	X	X	O

Answer:
1. Claire Danner/San Francisco/July 12th
2. Raj Patel/Atlanta/August 5th
3. Indira Nandi/Nashville/April 10th
4. Justin Bass/Honolulu/June 18th

WEDNESDAY Page 79
Mega Math
Paints cost $16.00.
Consonants are $3.00 each and vowels are $2.00 each.

Riddles
1. Snail
2. Fire
3. Mercury

THURSDAY Page 81
Progressive Words

PLATE
SLATE
STATE
STARE
STORE
STORM

This is a suggested answer. There may be more than one correct answer.

Famous People Facts
1. d   2. a   3. b   4. c

FRIDAY Word Puzzle Page 83

C	R	I	M	E
R	A	D	O	N
I	D	I	O	T
M	O	O	S	E
E	N	T	E	R

SATURDAY Page 84 – 85

Super Duper Chopper 'Copter
3. It drops straight down.
5. It spins slowly to the ground.
6. It makes the flight shorter, speeding up the descent. It also stabilizes the craft. Because of the added weight, more lift would be needed to slow down the 'copter's descent.

SUNDAY More Mega Math Page 86

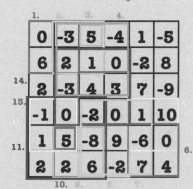

1. 6 + 2 – 3 + 0 = 5
2. 5 – 3 + 2 + 1 = 5
3. 5 = 5
4. 5 + 2 + 1 + 0 + 4 + 3 – 3 – 4 – 3 = 5
5. 10 + 1 – 6 + 0 = 5
6. 7 + 4 + 0 – 6 = 5
7. 0 + 1 + 9 + 6 + 7 – 2 – 8 – 6 – 2 = 5
8. 6 – 2 + 9 – 8 = 5
9. 5 + 2 + 6 – 8 = 5
10. 5 = 5
11. 2 + 2 + 6 – 8 + 5 + 1 – 1 + 0 – 2 = 5
12. 1 + 5 + 0 – 1 = 5
13. 4 + 3 + 0 – 2 = 5
14. 2 + 1 + 0 + 3 + 4 – 3 + 0 – 2 + 0 = 5

SUNDAY Word Pictures Page 86
1. split personality
2. lost in space
3. read between the lines
4. time in a bottle
5. strawberry shortcake
6. day after tomorrow
7. live and learn
8. light at the end of the tunnel

MONDAY Page 89

Answers will vary. Possible responses:
1. I might have taken a cell phone along to call for help.
2. Yes. The story has talked about bear and moose before this.
3. No. The situation is not much different from being in a campground.
4. Yes. I would have gotten bored and I would have wanted to help.
5. Getting under the truck is dangerous. They might be running out of supplies.
6. I think Trekk's dad will think of a way to get the truck loose.

TUESDAY Page 90
Math Maze

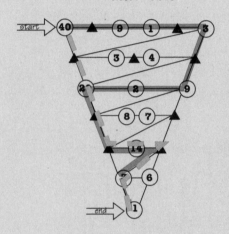

No Double Negatives
1. She didn't say anything.
2. There weren't any shoes left in my size.
3. He doesn't know anybody in his new school.
4. Don't leave any of the milk in your glass.

THURSDAY Read the Graph Page 94

1. November
2. February
3. $227.00
4. $380.92

TUESDAY Matching Page 91

1. e   2. h   3. d   4. g
5. f   6. c   7. b   8. a

WEDNESDAY Ultimate Scramble Page 92

1. Joker   4. Mischief   **Answer:**
2. Playful   5. Giggle   Wise Guy
3. Warped

WEDNESDAY Page 93

Mega Math

The football team has these coins:

12 silver dollars	$12.00
12 half dollars	$ 6.00
12 quarters	$ 3.00
12 dimes	$ 1.20
12 nickels	$ 0.60
12 pennies	$ 0.12
TOTAL	$22.92

Find the Percent of Each Number

1. 5% of 25 = 1.25
2. 16% of 26 = 4.16
3. 72% of 105 = 75.6
4. 11% of 5 = 0.55
5. 52% of 91 = 47.32
6. 33% of 99 = 32.67
7. 89% of 246 = 218.94
8. 20% of 10 = 2

THURSDAY Page 95
Progressive Words

CRAVE
GRAVE
GRADE
GLADE
GLIDE

This is a suggested answer. There may be more than one correct answer.

Famous People Facts

1. b   2. d   3. a   4. c

FRIDAY Page 97
Word Puzzle

D2 S	D5	B4 C	D4	A3 E	D3
A5	E1 O	D4	D1 C	B3	C3 R

WEEK 7 • Continued

SUNDAY   Page 100
More Mega Math

 = 4   = 5   ● = 3

Answer: ? = 8

Brain Teaser
a. Watermelon   d. Tennis racket
b. Flower   e. Artichoke
c. Garlic   f. Cheerios

WEEK 8 • Pages 100–113

SUNDAY Subject and Predicate   Page 101

1. My math book (is so heavy.)
2. The macaroni and cheese (tastes salty.)
3. Sara (fell on the playground.)
4. Bill (learned to waterski last summer.)
5. Mimi's sunglasses (are purple with silver sequins.)
6. I (baked a chocolate cake today.)
7. My dad's car (is being repaired.)
8. The towel (is still wet.)
9. I (have sand between my toes.)
10. Harold (played with his nephews.)

MONDAY   Crossword   Page 103

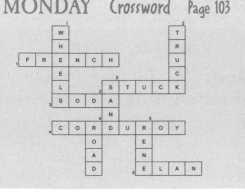

TUESDAY   Page 104
Odd Number Out

1st row: 82. All others are products of 9.
(9x1=9, 9x14=126, 9x5=45, 9x3=27)

2nd row: 12. All others are products of 8.
(8x1=8, 8x12=96, 8x6=48, 8x9=72)

OR   8, All others are products of 12.
(12x8=96, 12x4=48, 12x1=12, 12x6=72)

3rd row: 15. All others are products of 6.
(6x12=72, 6x6=36, 6x1=6, 6x9=54)

Matching   Page 105

1. e   5. a
2. f   6. b
3. d   7. c
4. h   8. g

Word Pictures

A. Hopscotch   E. Walking on water
B. Condensed milk   F. Green with envy
C. Water under the bridge   G. Surround sound
D. Banana split   H. Play by play

WEDNESDAY
Photo Match   Page 106

1. i   5. a   9. c
2. h   6. g   10. j
3. e   7. f   11. k
4. b   8. d   12. l

Mega Math   Page 107
The sleeping bag costs $28.00.
Multiply the number of consonants
by the number of vowels.

Riddles
1. Maryland   2. A river
3. Ohio   4. The letter "E"

THURSDAY   Estimation   Page 108

1.   100   4.   600   7.   400
    x 900   x 900   x 400
   900,000   540,000   160,000

2.   500   5.   600   8.   800
    x 500   x 700   x 800
   250,000   420,000   640,000

3.   100   6.   300
    x 100   x 200
    10,000   60,000

THURSDAY   Page 109
Progressive Words

HASTE   This is a suggested
PASTE   answer. There may
PASTY   be more than one
PATTY   correct answer.
PETTY

Famous People Facts
1. d   2. c   3. b   4. a

MONDAY Page 131

Answers will vary. Possible responses:
1. She turned it on and aimed it through the window.
2. He lifted the rear window of the truck.
3. He waved the light in the bears' faces, shouted at them, and then pounded on the tailgate of the truck.
4. One bear hit the side of the truck and scratched the bed rail.
5. The truck was dented and the side rail was scratched.
6. The cooler was destroyed, and the water jug was punctured.

TUESDAY Clueless Crossword Page 132

TUESDAY
Matching Page 133

1. d	5. f
2. h	6. b
3. e	7. a
4. g	8. c

WEDNESDAY
Photo Match Page 134

1. k	6. c	11. e
2. l	7. i	12. g
3. h	8. d	13. f
4. m	9. a	14. j
5. b	10. n	

WEDNESDAY Page 135

Mega Math
The wool sweater costs $52.00.
Vowels are worth $8.00 each and consonants are worth $2.00 each.

Riddle
1. A blink   2. A beetle

THURSDAY Word Pictures Page 136

A. walking side by side
B. oysters on the half shell
C. in between a rock and a hard place
D. eating on the run
E. once upon a time
F. down under
G. broken heart
H. downtown

THURSDAY Page 137
Progressive Words

VOWEL
TOWEL
TOWER
TOTER
TATER
LATER

This is a suggested answer.
There may be more than one correct answer.

Famous People Facts
1. d   2. a   3. b   4. c

FRIDAY Word Puzzle Page 139

P	A	R	T	S
A	D	O	R	E
R	O	B	I	N
T	R	I	E	D
S	E	N	D	S

SUNDAY Odd Number Out Page 142

1. 6/27
2. 24/100
3. 30/211

Cause and Effect Page 142

1. Cause: Sam failed his science test.
   Effect: Sam couldn't watch television for one week.

2. Cause: Ellen's grandma was very sick.
   Effect: Ellen made a get well card.

3. Cause: Rick's hair was hanging in his eyes.
   Effect: Rick got a haircut.

4. Cause: Amber loved to draw.
   Effect: Amber's mom got her art lessons.

MONDAY   Page 145

1. g   5. d
2. f   6. h
3. e   7. b
4. c   8. a

TUESDAY   Math Maze   Page 146

Answer: 84 ÷ 14 = 6 x 30 = 180
32 x 45 = 1440 ÷ 8 = 180

Antonyms, Synonyms or Homonyms

1. synonym   4. homonym
2. antonym   5. synonym
3. homonym   6. antonym

WEDNESDAY   Line Graph   Page 149

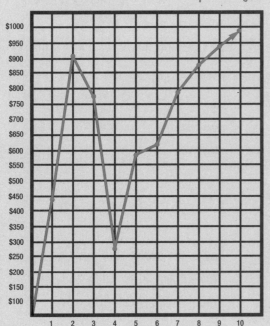

TUESDAY   Page 147
Matching

1. e   5. c
2. g   6. a
3. f   7. d
4. h   8. b

WEDNESDAY
Mega Math   Page 149

Kana has these bills:

6 twenties	$120.00
12 tens	$120.00
3 fives	$ 15.00
2 ones	$ 2.00
TOTAL	$257.00

Ultimate Scramble   Page 148

1. Milk   5. Eggs
2. Wisconsin   Answer:
3. Holstein   Swiss Cheese
4. Cream

THURSDAY   Page 150
Angles

1. acute
2. obtuse
3. right
4. acute
5. right
6. obtuse

THURSDAY –   Page 151
Progressive Words

JOKER
POKER
POWER   This is a suggested answer.
MOWER   There may be more than one correct answer.
MOWED
ROWED

Famous People Facts

1. b   2. c   3. d   4. a

FRIDAY Word Puzzle Page 153

C1 R	C4	B1 O	C5	C4 E	C1	E1	B5 L	D3
A1	D4 O	C5	E1 S	D2	B3 V	D2 E	A3	A4 T

SATURDAY Page 155
Testing Direction with Orville and Wilbur

Charting Directions: Changes to wing levels especially illustrate how lift and drag affect a plane's direction. Thrust would have an effect on flight distance only if the amount of muscle used to throw the plane varied.

WEEK 12 • Pages 158–173

MONDAY Page 159

4, 10, 1, 6, 7, 2, 8, 5, 3, 9

TUESDAY Page 161
Famous Inventors

1. c   5. h
2. e   6. d
3. g   7. a
4. b   8. f

TUESDAY Grid Logic Page 160

	Rodney	Byron	Robert	Isabella	Iris	Violin	Guitar	Drums	Trombone	Saxophone	Mr. Leeves	Mrs. Kim	Ms. Hasad	Mr. Owen	Miss Kraus
Gist	X	X	X	X	O	X	X	X	O	X	X	X	O	X	X
Rothschild	X	O	X	X	X	X	O	X	X	X	X	X	X	O	O
Sylvester	O	X	X	X	X	O	X	X	X	X	X	O	X	X	X
Templeton	X	X	O	X	X	X	X	O	X	X	X	X	X	O	X
Lane	X	X	X	O	X	X	X	X	O	O	X	X	X	X
Mr. Leeves	X	X	X	O	X	X	X	X	O
Mrs. Kim	O	X	X	X	X	O
Ms. Hasad	X	X	X	X	O	X
Mr. Owen	X	X	O	X	X
Miss Kraus	X	O	X	X	X
Violin	O	X	X	X
Guitar	X	O	X	X
Drums	X	X	O	X
Trombone	X	X	X	X	O
Saxophone	X	X	X	O	X

Answer:
1. Rodney Sylvester/Violin/Mrs. Kim
2. Byron Rothschild/Guitar/Miss Kraus
3. Robert Templeton/Drums/Mr. Owen
4. Isabella Lane/Saxophone/Mr. Leeves
5. Iris Gist/Trombone/Ms. Hasad

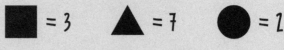

SUNDAY Page 156
More Mega Math

■ = 3   ▲ = 7   ● = 2

Answer: ? = 14

Brain Teaser

a. Rubber bands   d. Spools of thread
b. Peanuts   e. Sponge
c. Pasta   f. Pipecleaners

SUNDAY Page 157
Word Problems

1. 700,000 x 0.80 = 560,000 T-shirts
2. 22 students per class
3. 14 rides
4. 104 gallons
5. $53.00
6. 14:6, 10:10

WEDNESDAY Page 162
Odd Number Out

1st row: 54. All others are products of 7.
(7 x 16 = 112, 7 x 12 = 84, 7 x 7 = 49, 7 x 41 = 287)

2nd row: 73. All others are products of 8.
(8 x 11 = 88, 8 x 21 = 168, 8 x 12 = 96, 8 x 15 = 120)

3rd row: 104. All others are products of 3.
(3 x 6 = 18, 3 x 66 = 198, 3 x 9 = 27, 3 x 39 = 117)

Word Games

1. They are all English kings.
2. They are all invertebrates.
3. They are all carnivores.

WEDNESDAY Page 163
Mega Math

The comic books cost $10.00.
Vowels are $1.75 each and consonants are $0.50 each.

THURSDAY Page 164
Word Pictures

A. square dance
B. raining cats and dogs
C. safety in numbers
D. the proof is in the pudding
E. man in the moon
F. books on tape
G. countdown
H. milkshake
I. apple turnover
J. mailbox
K. scattered showers
L. back in time
M. working overtime
N. too little too late
O. two of a kind
P. mashed potatoes

THURSDAY Page 165
Progressive Words

PANTS
RANTS
RUNTS
RUSTS
RUSTY

This is a suggested answer.
There may be more than one correct answer.

Famous People Facts

1. b   2. d   3. a   4. c

FRIDAY Page 167
Word Puzzle

SUNDAY Page 170

Adjectives and Predicate Adjectives

1. A   2. B   3. A   4. B   5. B   6. A

SUNDAY
Point of View   Page 171

1. third   2. first   3. first   4. third
5. third   6. first   7. third   8. first

How to solve
Grid Logic problems...

Grid logic is a fun way to figure out what traits or facts should be paired together, based on a series of clues that have been given. The key part of solving a grid logic problem is the grid. As you read the questions, use the grid to mark with an "X" traits that you know don't go together. For example, if the clue is "Emily and the Phillips child live near each other," you can put an X in the box that pairs "Emily" and "Phillips" together, because you now know they are two separate people. Make sure to pay close attention to the clues that are given. For example, if the clue says, "the Turner boy..." you know to mark an "X" by any girl's name that intersects with Turner. The clue just told you that the Turner child is a boy, not a girl. If you know that two traits DO go together, you can mark the intersecting box with an "O." The following is an example of a grid logic problem. Let's solve it together.

Mary and her friends went to the pool. While they were there, they each swam laps using a different stroke. Based on the clues below, can you determine each child's first and last name and the type of stroke they used?

1. Mary and the Waters girl both ride their bikes to the pool.
2. The boy who swam the breaststroke has the same initial for his first and last name.
3. The child who swam freestyle, Mary, and the Holland child all live in the same neighborhood.
4. Christopher swam a stroke named after an insect.

	Mary	Cecily	Christopher	Jon	Backstroke	Freestyle	Breaststroke	Butterfly
Jones								
Waters								
Holland								
Warner								
Backstroke								
Freestyle								
Breaststroke								
Butterfly								

1. Mary and the Waters girl both ride their bikes to the pool.

This clue tells us that Mary's last name is not Waters, so we place an "X" in the box that intersects "Mary" and "Waters." It also tells us that the Waters child is a girl, so we can also place an "X" in the boxes that intersect "Waters" with "Christopher" and "Jon," because they are not girls.

By doing that, it is clear that the Waters child is Cecily, so we can place an "O" in that box. We can also place an "X" in the boxes that cross Cecily with the other last names: Jones, Holland, and Warner.

	Mary	Cecily	Christopher	Jon	Backstroke	Freestyle	Breaststroke	Butterfly
Jones								
Waters	X		X	X				
Holland								
Warner								
Backstroke								
Freestyle								
Breaststroke								
Butterfly								

	Mary	Cecily	Christopher	Jon	Backstroke	Freestyle	Breaststroke	Butterfly
Jones		X						
Waters	X	O	X	X				
Holland		X						
Warner		X						
Backstroke								
Freestyle								
Breaststroke								
Butterfly								

2. The boy who swam the breaststroke has the same initial for his first and last name.

The only first and last names that have the same initial are "Jon" and "Jones," so we can place an "O" in that box and an "X" in the others.

We can also place an "O" in the boxes that intersect "Jon" and "Jones" with "breaststroke."

	Mary	Cecily	Christopher	Jon	Backstroke	Freestyle	Breaststroke	Butterfly
Jones	X	X	X	O				
Waters	X	O	X	X				
Holland		X		X				
Warner		X		X				
Backstroke								
Freestyle								
Breaststroke								
Butterfly								

	Mary	Cecily	Christopher	Jon	Backstroke	Freestyle	Breaststroke	Butterfly
Jones	X	X	X	O	X	X	O	X
Waters	X	O	X	X			X	
Holland		X		X			X	
Warner		X		X			X	
Backstroke				X				
Freestyle				X				
Breaststroke	X	X	X	O				
Butterfly				X				

3. The child who swam freestyle, Mary, and the Holland child all live in the same neighborhood.

This clue tells us that Mary's last name is not Holland. By placing an "X" in that box, we find out that Mary's last name is Warner and Christopher's is Holland.

It also tells us that Mary (Warner) and (Christopher) Holland did not swim freestyle. By crossing out those boxes, we discover that it was Cecily who swam freestyle.

	Mary	Cecily	Christopher	Jon	Backstroke	Freestyle	Breaststroke	Butterfly
Jones	X	X	X	O	X	X	O	X
Waters	X	O	X	X	X	O	X	X
Holland	X	X	O	X		X	X	
Warner	O	X	X	X		X	X	
Backstroke		X		X				
Freestyle	X	O	X	X				
Breaststroke	X	X	X	O				
Butterfly		X		X				

4. Christopher swam a stroke named after an insect.

The only stroke named after an insect is the "butterfly" and this clue tells us that Christopher is the one who swam it. After matching "Christopher" with the "butterfly," we discover that Mary is the child who swam the backstroke.

	Mary	Cecily	Christopher	Jon	Backstroke	Freestyle	Breaststroke	Butterfly
Jones	X	X	X	O	X	X	O	X
Waters	X	O	X	X	X	O	X	X
Holland	X	X	O	X		X	X	
Warner	O	X	X	X		X	X	
Backstroke		X		X				
Freestyle	X	O	X	X				
Breaststroke	X	X	X	O				
Butterfly		X		X				

The grid is now complete and it gives us these answers: Mary Warner swam backstroke, Cecily Waters swam freestyle, Christopher Holland swam butterfly, and Jon Jones swam breaststroke.

	Mary	Cecily	Christopher	Jon	Backstroke	Freestyle	Breaststroke	Butterfly
Jones	X	X	X	O	X	X	O	X
Waters	X	O	X	X	X	O	X	X
Holland	X	X	O	X	X	X	X	O
Warner	O	X	X	X	O	X	X	X
Backstroke	O	X	X	X				
Freestyle	X	O	X	X				
Breaststroke	X	X	X	O				
Butterfly	X	X	O	X				

Answer:
Mary Warner/Backstroke
Cecily Waters/Freestyle
Christopher Holland/Butterfly
Jon Jones/Breaststroke

Notes

EXPLORING FLIGHT

ORVILLE & WILBUR WRIGHT
(1871-1948, 1867-1912)

Wilbur and Orville Wright were two brothers who shared a sense of ingenuity and a common dream. During the late 19th century, the idea of flight seemed ridiculous and was actually very dangerous. Many early flight aviators died in their attempts, but the Wright brothers were convinced they could do it. They were so convinced that they gave up any idea of a social life, or marriage, so that they could concentrate all their energies on the flight quest.

The two brothers began with experiments on gliders, but what they really longed to achieve was controlled flight by a machine that used its own power, not the power of the wind. After many experiments, the Wright brothers were ready for their first engine-powered flight. They chose to test their "flying machine" in December, 1903, in Kitty Hawk, North Carolina. The first flight ended in mishap when a part called the skid snapped. Three days later, airplane fixed, Orville made the historic flight. It only lasted 12 seconds, but it was the first time in history that a self-powered machine carried a man forward into free flight, without losing speed, and landed without injury. Those 12 seconds marked the beginning of modern aviation.

AMELIA EARHART
(1897-1937)

No one will ever know exactly what happened to Amelia Earhart. Earhart was the first person to fly from Hawaii to California. She was the first woman to fly cross-country over the United States. As a young girl, Earhart had always wanted to go higher and faster. She'd even built a modified roller coaster in her backyard.

She wanted to be the first to fly around the widest part of the world—the equator. She set off with her navigator, Fred Noonan, and the two began their journey, first from Miami to San Juan, Puerto Rico. Stopping at different sites along the way, they flew over Africa, India, Australia, and made it to New Guinea. The next leg of their journey was to get to Howland, a tiny island surrounded by miles of ocean. She never made it. Radio contact was lost and search crews were unable to find any sign of her or her plane.

CHARLES LINDBERGH
(1902-1974)

Charles Lindbergh flew his plane, the "Spirit of St. Louis," from New York to Paris in 33 hours. It was the first solo transatlantic flight.

As a young man, Lindbergh was a "barnstormer." Barnstormers were daredevils who charged set prices for stunts like head-on collisions with cars, crashing planes into trees, and flying upside down with a man on the landing gear.

As an airmail pilot, between Chicago and St. Louis, Lindbergh heard about a $25,000 prize for the first person to complete a flight across the Atlantic Ocean without stopping. Some St. Louis businessmen invested in the project and the Ryan Aircraft company built the "Spirit of St. Louis."

Taking off from New York, Lindbergh carried only a compass, four sandwiches, two canteens of water, 451 gallons (1707 liters) of gas and a chart balanced on his knees. During the flight, he battled fatigue and bone-chilling cold. There was no heater and Lindbergh flew low over icebergs and the vast Atlantic Ocean. He landed in Paris, on May 21, 1927, as a celebrity. He was only 25 years old. After the historic flight, his life was marked by controversy and tragedy.

THE HINDENBURG
"Oh, the Humanity"

The Hindenburg was a famous dirigible. A dirigible (or zeppelin) was a flying machine made of several balloons inside a rigid structure. These balloons were filled with hydrogen, an extremely flammable fuel. Zeppelins were huge structures. At a length of 803 feet (244.8 m), the Hindenburg was almost the length of the Titanic. It remains the largest airship to ever have cruised the skies.

Tickets for the flight were $400, the price of a small car in those days. For that price, passengers were fed freshly prepared food, slept in their own rooms and could even shower.

The Hindenburg left Germany, carrying 61 crew members and 36 passengers. It flew over the airfield in New Jersey for a routine landing. Suddenly, something ignited the hydrogen that filled the great balloons. It took only seconds for the burning Hindenburg to crash to the ground. Twenty-two crewmen, 13 passengers, and one member of the ground crew died. Radio reporter, Herb Morrison, watching from the ground, cried, "It's burst into flames…Oh, the humanity, and all the passengers…"

EXPLORING FLIGHT

EXPLORING FLIGHT

JACKIE COCHRAN
(Around 1906-1980)

She didn't own a pair of shoes until she was eight, but by the time Jackie Cochran died, she'd held more aviation records than anyone, male or female, in speed, altitude and distance. As a child, she often slept on the floor and went hungry. Cochran was giving permanent waves in a beauty salon by the time she was thirteen. Years later, while living in New York City, a friend suggested she learn to fly. As soon as she took her first lesson, Jackie Cochran knew she was an aviator. She began entering contests and winning them. She was the first woman to pilot a military bomber across the Atlantic Ocean. She founded the WASPs (Women's Airforce Service Pilots) during WWII, and was awarded the Distinguished Service Medal for her actions during WWII. After the war, she was the first woman to break the sound barrier. Other pilots looked at Jackie Cochran as a pilot who wasn't there for the glory—she was just trying to see how fast she could go.

CHUCK YEAGER
(1923-present)

In 1947, the agency that would become NASA tested a plane they thought could go faster than the speed of sound (around 650 mph or 1046 kmph). Chuck Yeager, a test pilot, was experienced and cool under pressure. At 20,000 feet (6096 m) the X-1 was released from the B-29 that carried it (built for speed, the X-1 was only able to fly for 3 minutes, so it needed another craft to get it to a higher altitude). The machmeter, used to measure the plane's speed, seemed to go haywire. It was made to go up to Mach 1. Yeager went up to Mach 1.07. He was the first to go faster than the speed of sound.

THE CONCORDE

The Concorde was a supersonic plane that traveled at speeds of about 1,490 miles (2,398 km) per hour—more than twice the speed of sound! A Boeing 747 has a top speed of 604 miles (972 km) per hour. At its cruising altitude of 60,000 feet (18,288 m), passengers could see the curvature of the earth! A regular jet takes about 8 hours to get from New York to London. The Concord made the same trip in less than 3 hours. Commercial service began in 1976 and ended in 2003 due to the high cost of maintaining the planes.

JOHN GLENN JR.
(1921-present)

John Glenn was a member of the original group of NASA astronauts, the Mercury Seven. (M. Scott Carpenter, L. Gordon Cooper, Jr., Virgil (Gus) Grissom, Walter M. (Wally) Schirra, Jr., Alan B. Shepard, Jr., and Donald K. (Deke) Slayton.) On February 20, 1962, Glenn became the first American to orbit the Earth. After 4 hours, 55 minutes and 23 seconds, and 3 rotations around the Earth, Glenn landed the Friendship 7 safely in the Pacific Ocean. After his time as an astronaut, Glenn was successful in politics. In 1998, the 77-year-old Glenn went up in space again, as a member of the space shuttle Discovery.

THE MOON LANDING

On July 20, 1969, people all over the world gathered in front of their televisions, near their radios, and in each other's homes. Mankind was crossing the final frontier. The Apollo 11 entered the moon's orbit. Neil Armstrong and Edwin "Buzz" Aldrin boarded the Eagle, a landing craft designed to take them to the moon's surface. Michael Collins stayed behind, in the command module. Six and a half hours later, Armstrong was the first to crawl out of the capsule. As his boots touched the moon's surface, he said, "That's one small step for man— one giant leap for mankind."

THE STEALTH BOMBER

Radar technology makes it possible to locate the position, shape and often speed of an airplane. Objects reflect radio waves the same way they reflect light. The way a particular object reflects radio waves is called a radar signature. Although its wingspan is half the size of a football field, the B-2 Stealth Bomber is virtually invisible to radar because of its reduced radar signature. Many other features that make the B-2 Stealth Bomber "stealthy" are classified by the U.S. Government.

INTERNATIONAL SPACE STATION

The International Space Station is being built by 16 different countries: the United States, Canada, Russia, Brazil, Japan and a group of nations known as the European Space Agency (Belgium, Britain, Denmark, France, Germany, Italy, Norway, Spain, Sweden, Switzerland and the Netherlands). Life on the ISS is very different from life on Earth. Astronauts witness 15 dawns per day. They have to attach their sleeping bags to a wall to keep from floating into station equipment. Dinner is sometimes soup served in plastic bags. At the end of a busy day, astronauts can look out on the view that makes it all worth it: the Earth rotating on its axis.